Nevada Beach

Poems and Kindred Works

Richard Alan Bunch

∞ INFINITY
PUBLISHING

Copyright © 2016 by Richard Alan Bunch

ISBN 978-1-4958-1280-4

Published December 2016

∞

INFINITY PUBLISHING
1094 New DeHaven Street, Suite 100
West Conshohocken, PA 19428-2713
Toll-free (877) BUY BOOK
Local Phone (610) 941-9999
Fax (610) 941-9959
Info@buybooksontheweb.com
www.buybooksontheweb.com

To the memory of my parents and sister

and to

Rita, Katharine, and Rick

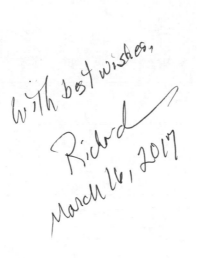

With best wishes,

Richard

March 16, 2017

Grateful acknowledgement is to the following editors and publishers in whose publications (including online) earlier or final versions of some of these poems and prose first appeared: *The Plaza, Writers of the Purple Sage, Goose River Anthology, Language and Cultural Review.*

In addition, grateful acknowledgement is made to my wife, Rita, for her helpful support, suggestions, and also pictures of the author in each of these volumes.

Μή, φίλα ψὐχά, βίον ἀθάνάτον οπευδε, τάν δἐμπρακτον
ἀντλει μαχανάν.

— Pindar, Pythian Odes

(My soul, do not seek immortal life, but exhaust the realm
of the possible.)

Mais où sont les neiges d'antan?

(But where are the snows of yesteryear?)

— François Villon, *Ballade of the Ladies of Bygone Times*

Contents

Contents

Poems

Stories

Creative Nonfiction

Poems

Forever Leaving

After reading some poems
by Anna Hajnal
and Natalya Gorbanyevskaya,
I look up
and begin to realize
we dwell
in a breath of language
that soon leaves us.

In fact, when I invite
a gesture of insight,
it flatly states
that throughout our lives,
in this wandering universe,
we are forever leaving.

Just ask a graveyard drunk,
raven rhymes
with a serpent's tongue,
migratory monarchs,
a mantled skull
with purple-tinted sockets,
the ticking baggage
of divine time,
the bones
of unconscious poetry,
even in the *Times,*
swinging in the wind,
and dinosaurs in swamps.

This ritual is more
ancient than we realize.

Editing

Should you wish
to edit
the film of our vanity,
we realize
each is a door
that can open
to water shining
among the castanets
that sometimes wrestle
with the wind.

As a token
of the dim frontiers
of our birth,
we understand how
audio waves lift
two hundred ton rocks
precisely into place
engineered
during the Paleolithic Age
and remark
the way
wrinkled mountains
may wake as cumulus clouds.

As for me, I enjoy
sunlit lanes, the
massive soul of
seaboard sand grains,
breath that connects
even us
in the audio waves
pronounced in
the lexicon of galaxies
and leaves swaying
in a summer breeze.

Appassionato April

After you draw
a jet set model
with her hot pink
and black lips parted,
dreams flutter over
the fairest wave
that rides the sea
as it washes away
your drawing.

Later, as you walk
the dog in the park,
you greet others
with "Namaste"
and "Peace, bro"

In the vibrancies of
appassionato April
and among
quivering pigeons,
you watch as our river
runs into an estuary
known as Nowhere
Zen New Mexico
on the edges
of moonrise.

Sometimes, beneath
a blanket
of dragonflies and wind,
our lives bristle
with the resounding
ashes of loneliness.

Lita

She dresses with damask spins
of raiment from some
foreign night
beneath a stubble
of silvery stars.

At times she dresses
as the tides
riled by the moon
in cloth that translates
her feelings
like violins
in four accents
even when
grand dames
and unstubbled codgers
are there.

They admire
her flower garden
with yellow and violet tulips
and fresh irises
that welcome
admiring eyes
beneath a lapis lazuli sky.

She is a lyric forever
and more
than a mere husk
of scarlet-hued dreams.

Fiddler Crabs

Along a coast
of weathered stone,
sea grass,

and living sand
with fiddler crabs,
morning wind unfolds
a prairie of wildflowers
along a fence
whose spines
read the smell
of summer grasses.

As semis and flying
cars rata-tat-tat
the highway
speckled with
truth's wide angles,
we sense language
layers not only
tiny chains
of original protein
but off-shore skerries
where sea birds feed.

Soon I stop at *God Only Knows*
for apples, bananas,
raspberries, spaghetti,
and tonic water with quinine.

High in the hills,
I can hear
the canyon's pitch
that soon summer
will vanish
as swift as a comet
on a starless night.

Open a Hole

There's a reckoning
of wider worlds
with unsettled gravity,

serpents with souls,
faces washed
in a shimmer
of luscious light
that becomes
a toast
to tawny antiquity
wooed by time,
marketplaces for wars
of a different kind,
muffled voices of evil
and pearl tears
drifting us
to madness.

Sometimes we forget
we are just mortals
in a dream in a depth
of field
in which grass seeds
planted are felt
in faraway places,
including bays
with several estuaries.

Sometimes you just
have to open a hole
and behold a sky
the color
of a deep rose's vermillion.

Singer of Lesbos

As oars plash toward the shore,
amid the wind's erratic will,
we muse
on the radiant verses and
archaic beauty of Sappho.

While our flesh
oozes toward a bellowing sun,
we remember how her poetry
unearths flowerings of eros,
wedding parties,
the naked beauty of eyes,
broken hearts,
lyre-strummed songs
about true love,
prayers to Aphrodite,
and sea winds in olive tree leaves.

In these trying times,
her poems and songs
bring order and beauty.

Revival

All over this particular earth
the sun writes things
in lemon yellow
palm tree light
even as birch pollen
sullies sidewalks
and genital waves
lap our shores
with a white water blush.

Periodically we realize
there must be a revival
of the wormwood pain
of amour
despite rising winds.

That is when we begin
our trek homeward
to the original ardor
past sandbar dusks,
hoof beats of unshod horses,

and tangerine suits
with ruffs and spangles.

Then we do more
than sniff and make smiley faces.

Nightmares

As a wandering wind
wrinkles a summer hillside
with the perfume
of latitude,
she recounts
the story
of his abiding inscape
that fears
the war-zone abyss
envisioned in his nightmares.

She assures him sleep,
deep sleep
can cushion his fear.

But between whistling
ducks whistling and
the rooster's "chicchirici,"
it is amazing
he gets any sleep at all.

She also recommends
he avoid caffeine
and sleeping pills
and focus instead
on the history of starlight
and sunless river bottoms.

Imagery springing
from the sea
and mountains

can have
a camphor-like effect
on nasal passages
that may change
his mood and allow
him to relax.

All this
is going down
as a white dove
perches
in the cypress
next to the lemon grove.

Wave Skipper

As we walked at dusk
along a river
that seemed to be playing
down the piano scales,
we noticed
a hull mottled with rust
of a tugboat
named *Wave Skippper*
this far inland.

And from the Falstaff Café
came the aroma
of flowering thyme
as a thin white moon
rose in the pepper tree
and crickets resounded
like lightning
lashing the earth.

When it comes
to dreams of the future,
tomorrow we will explore
terra incognita

where supposedly
the present king of France
wears a goatee
and has a a mistress
that turns the turning world.

Desire Pursued

As daylight crackles
and summer hues
dance on the decks
of harbor boats,
we savor wild honey,
violin notes,
and symbolic songs
of ourselves
as in the hypocrisy
of some ascetics
who swear off desire
and swim
in dung-filled rivers.

One of our instinctive
ventures
is to live
amid bloomy-leafed
traveller's joy
and pink poppies
and ask
"O desire, where is thy end?"

The pursuit of desire
is a naked pursuit forever
since we assume
the obvious
is going to hug us
as we watch
a dove's curve in flight.

Desire can also rise
from the sea
to effect a semi-global joy.

Sarangi Sounds

We take our oaten bread,
coffee, and pure
mountain water
and head
beneath
a thinning armature
of fog to the coast.

Once the fog lifts,
we realize
no compass rose
is needed
on our map
of the seashore
of endless worlds.

Stones migrate
out of the waves
to the sounds
of a forty-stringed
sarangi
as the sea surges
with laughter
beneath bronze
breaker brows.

Far out at sea,
tempests roam
as cicadas sing
and we note
the scent
of color swirls
by the garden

where white roses
and bluebonnets grow.

A nearby hill
is an island
patched with
mushrooms
and wild blackberries.

After we absorb
the aromas
of land, sea, and sky,
we head back
to our cabin
beneath a rococo moonlight.

Call of the Flesh

Between two tamarinds
on a tropical afternoon,
we answer the call
of the flesh
and kiss.

We also hear the
humming of the sea
and notice a rebel flag
that flaps
in the breeze
and in the dream
of water birds
within a sheet of sunlight
that freckles our shadows
within a wave.

Nearby are huge purple figs,
a field with the aroma
of newly-cut hay,
lupines that loll in the breezes,

and grassy hillocks
where black angus bulls nibble.

Herring gulls and kestrels
add to the sea's language
in a tumult
of lost tribe mouths
as we realize
so many worlds
are at hand.

Dead Time

As we toast
with a glass
brimming with Russians,
we know
how truth
can confound us
on a journey
of night watchmen,
guinea fowls,
damsels of the night,
and glass blowers.

We stand
on a balcony
overlooking the sea
and espy coral reefs
as you read tomorrow's
newspaper.

It has been a longish day
and you are
a smile that maps
lassitude
among the drifts
of dead time.

A glass of red wine
still helps us glimpse,
in our fields of contemplation,
a unity of blood
and bones
in the scorpio sky.

Planting Season

At our quiet coastal house
in the country,
we plant garlic bulbs
and sweet-smelling marjoram
by white fence posts
as we hear the unceasing
twitter of shearwater birds.

In my daydreams
hidden in time,
I caress your tenderness
and admire your veins
of a great wisdom
as we walk along
in yellow sandals
over ever-sustaining
roots
of onlooking blossoms
that witness,
in whiplashes of light,
the arranged flowers
that often pass
like trains,
even in hospitals,
through our lives.

One must have
a patience of granite
to gain a perspective

on such sweet
geometries in flower.

Unne

Flaunting fortune,
a young philosopher
with a fatuous smile
and earthly thoughts
caboosed behind
summer squalls
at last realizes
rudeness impeaches
itself
since attachment
leavens its own gravity.

Despite a raging sea
and its
mossed-granite rocks
dripping with foam,
a mocha girl
in her greenest flower
dazzles him
with tender caresses.

All her flowering
is deeded to their
enchanted time together
and maples stamped
with the west,
not to mention
sea green calderas
of the lawns
as she fixes him tea
and hot apple pie.

Liquid Lingering

At the realm's hem,
you can view
planetary originals
such as a glacier
gangling through
a hawk's wild dream
or a jungle of ocean's
deepest green trees
laired in
the dream of return.

There's a liquid lingering
in the fuchsia of solitude
and the ancient tracks
of serpentine time's
variations on a theme
of returns.

A sunflower of the winds
dances like Mali's princesses
as clouds sweep eastward
from the bible west.

Channel Buoys

Included in our body's tale
are whispers that secrete,
a howling in the mind,
blood flowing
behind lidded eyes,
and melodic beats
of stations.

We are standing by white birches
whimsical with
horned larks

and black-blue dragonflies
as we note
river runs
with their countless
elements
whose ripples flow
past laws, myths,
divinities,
and civilizations.

Such are the vibes
of channel buoys
and the splendors of whatever.

Fortune's Joke

We mark that sea-humming
island of Bosnian pines,
novitiate ibises,
and cicadas
who drone their
tastes of time
amid the scent of bells.

On these shores,
dirges of a vanishing summer
are the color
of the shipwreck *Fortune's Joke.*

Among manifestos
beneath the sea
are dialogues between
incognitos who engage
in concentric bosh
and votive flames
of fallen leaves of the sea.

The shoreline here
is mottled

with a saffron yellow
sun beneath
a pale blue sky.

Garden Party

Depending on which party I go to,
scandal sheets
cover them
with more odors
than selective fictions
can name.

Some women
dream of seducing young boys
and driving a red Tesla
that can fly.

Others adore the vibes
of castratos
through their
earth smoke of songs.

I hop a Greyhound
to Boston
and ponder the idea
that evil
is good's first invention
as I note
the moon mash
of late summer
and that leaves
do not always fall
in the fall.

Also, I attest
that daylight adulterers
and terrorists
are among the usual

curses of our time
as cherry blossoms,
white as snow beards
on a wintry moon,
begin to fall.

Shipless Sails

Out of a pouring dark
purged by epitaphs,
morning stars fade,
as does the
albino brush of moon
over an untouched forest
whipped into an olive green,
musselled rocks,
and disheveled sand.

A station of pines
and greenwood boughs
groan with the windscape.

Armed with weathered
fingers,
the poet as maestro
orchestrates
a deepening
of yellow sea foam
beneath a sky of wedgewood blue.

If you keep watching,
you can see shipless sails
and hear silence
between the stars
in an unphrased music.

Forecast

On beaches of flesh
and contented with little,
they avoid the disease
of unfeeling silence
and the ship
Greed of the Raider
marooned on the coast.

As light vibrates in triangles
on the estuary's nape,
they talk with granite
and birch trees
and note girls
with baskets of fish
and bottles of red wine.

They know our sleep
is a forgetting's birth
that unwrinkles the stars
and is daily tested
by sensual delight.

Cumuli with their
scudding thunderstorms
drench the morning stars
and pining pines
on the mountains.

Tomorrow's forecast:
a sunrise
of blameless joy.

Mountain Dreams

As I close my book
in the light of a lobster red sun,

I soon doze off
into the coral flowers
and turquoise blue horses
of dreams
warm with mediterranean colors.

Always there appears
a parabolic trajectory
with emerald green appetites
that grow into impulses
of a mountain
for I feel a serene passion
and joy among the mountains,
especially those
spangled with
the music of touch
amid the mountains
of cinnamon days.

Below, I see
the heartfelt esophagus
detour of the valley
and hear a gun's
loudmouthed concussion,
kelp being delightfully sucked
out of a sturgeon,
and a waltzing lunch bag
with green
and yellow eyes carved on it
buffeted by desert breezes.

Stories

Kismet

Whenever you would enter the large wall-filled library of Mr. Kismet, you would come out with the feeling of having seen a lifetime in only a few moments. It was like any other room I guess except that there pervaded in it a strangeness, a peculiar romance about it, that made it somehow different. The walls on the left were dotted with diplomas, certificates of all kinds conferring upon Mr. Kismet a sense of belonging, a sense of dignity that belonged solely to him. Somehow everything he associated with came out to grasp you and shake you out of the cornerstones of reality in favor of leisurely pipedreams.

With his hair graying about the temples, his eyes a merry and arrogant black, his jowls sagging slightly with age, Mr. Kismet cut a fine elderly picture. Out of the fog-enshrouded Jersey city of Princeton, he had shipped off to the German front in the first World War, all the while when behind the lines secretly courting the fairest frauleins imaginable, spending silent nights along the moon-swept waters of the slow-moving Rhine.

What fascinated me about his little cubbyhole of a room was that the very walls themselves seemed to whisper secrets of his past, a past more fascinating than fiction could muster the courage and audacity to spit out onto the printed page.

His son was my age and every day, through all the years of our acquaintance, he would take me into that room as if urging, quietly and subtly urging me, to put it into the inky markings of my prose.

No college degree supported him and I do not think Mr. Kismet gave a damn. He had come out of the stuffy high-class Princeton area with his family either having gone to Princeton or Rutgers through the last couple of generations. He had seen enough of all that.

I remember how we would watch him sitting there by the crackling fire and his eyes would look so sad, his head tilting over with sleep as if tired from doing a daily project that kept our imaginations alive with inquiry, to ourselves, of course. Every New Years that fire would burn like a lost youth in his eyes, his wife Oona sitting there with a highball in her hands, and spilling out gab that would make the Blarney Stone blush. But she danced, her eyes did, the fire crackled and popped and then midnight would strike and we would sing "Auld Lang Syne" with bravado, the ice in the glasses clinking as our arms waved high on the air.

Always after the party was over, and the gossiping, Mr. Kismet would depart for bed, his wife following easily and sleepily, leaving me with his son with whom I played hearts and black jack late into the dawn hours. The room stood there almost inviting us with its long arms of the past bidding us to come but with a dash of aloofness that urged us in. Every type of book conceivable for a literary mind lined his shelves: mysteries, science fiction, poetry, dramas, novels, stories of all kinds beckoned an avid reader to open their covers and partake of the print over which Mr. Kismet's eyes had swept.

Tucked within each book were mementoes and dates from 1909 to the stock market crash of 1929. Pictures of his first wife, Halfrida, were glued in the back cover, the one he had married after coming back to the states from the front. New Orleans, the "Big Easy," was his first stop. He adored the Latin Quarter; it reminded him so much of Paris. And how could you not love Paris?

While in Mississippi, he had met and talked with "Count No-Account," the nickname for the young William Faulkner. He also courted two Ole Miss coeds who are married to Memphis physicians to this day.

Halfrida was a partner in business with him but it did not last and so they split and he wandered, through Kansas City, the Ozarks of Missouri, the flat land around Detroit, the wavy fields of Nebraska, through the salt-saturated lake of Utah and through the desert interlude of Nevada and settled in the San Francisco Bay Area. It was in San Francisco that he painted huge yellow and red canvases, wrote his poetry for an anthology of forty-four California poets and married Oona from Pleasant Hill.

I remember his son asking him one evening how he liked the literature and poetry he had written.

"It's fine, I guess. Too damn much trouble pouring out your life on it though. I'd rather read the authors already on the market, the established ones like Carl Sandburg, Robinson Jeffers, Jack London, F. Scott Fitzgerald, Norris and the rest.

"Dad, did you ever write anything but poetry?" asked his freckle-faced son.

"A story here and there. It wasn't worth much. Too little time and I needed the money," he said, nodding all the while.

Mr. Kismet was a classy, well-mannered gentleman, dark, handsome and elderly. But very soon he died of a heart attack and he was buried on a sweet-scented grassy slope overlooked by hanging willow trees.

We cleaned up his room, and while putting his books in order we came across a burnished manuscript, its pages yellowish-brown from age. Dusting it off, we tried to make out the writing, scratched in black ink and labeled 1931. It was the torn fragments of a novel set on the German front with the 2nd Division of the United States forces at the battle of Chateau-Thierry when the German advance was broken. It was entirely autobiographical; his thoughts and sentiments about war and about life. It told of his being brought up in a middle class neighborhood in New Jersey, his conflicts with his father, his wanderings all over the continent, his enlistment in the service and his round about journey to California. Perhaps the most impressive portion of the manuscript was about the war, the futile days and nights when, at any moment, he could be shot and left a bloody carcass in a trench or foxhole. But in the margin he left a special message; in a different color of ink; not faded like the others in the manuscript as if he had written it only days before his death. It read:

"After life, war is hell. When all the sweet dawns and sunsets have departed, 'tis sweetest in death; then you only wage war with your soul."

We looked baffled at one another, the manuscript spread on his desk. When we went up the grassy slope to put roses on his grave the following Saturday, the ground looked as though it had been ground up, the dirt spread out like a fan. Apparently the gravestone had been moved. Lying in a clump of moist earth ten feet away from the burial site was an exact facsimile of that novel manuscript, the torn pages flipping this way and that way in the wind.

Our eyes, we thought, were deceiving us. Someone had marked the gravestone. It had his name Orville Kismet, dates 1891-1957, and then mysteriously it read: "suffering is the way of the world."

We put the roses gently on the grave and walked away, both of us, turning at every few steps to see the novel flapping in the wind and the flowers blowing this way. How the novel got there, no one knew. Or would ever know.

Veiled Interlude

O utside the pub, fog continued to further diminish the faint glow of the darkening sun. Inside, Wendy waited on some gents dressed in gray, brown, and blue Scottish tweeds, their faces ruddy, their talk a quiet hum. Methodically, she poured tall glasses of lager, ale, and stout until thick foam formed at the top. Though her brown eyes were calm, she had a faintly mischievous smile. Handsome in his army uniform, or so his mother once said, Aaron sat there and could not take his eyes off of her. He had done this before, although he was not becoming a nuisance about it. He simply liked her and their conversations on previous nights. The night before he decided she was for him; he liked her lips — the way they formed an alluring heart-shape — not to mention her straight black hair and that hint of Britannia in her demeanor that on these blackout nights possessed a touching warmth.

She came over and smiled for she recognized him as one of the Yanks she had met nights before and the one man she liked having a conversation with. The Yanks were stationed here to help fight the Nazi menace that could still use its control of northern France to threaten this little island "set in the silver sea." They had a spirited conversation the night before and when, in a moment of loneliness and near despair, he had asked her to have a drink with him after work. She did.

"Let's see if I remember," she teased Aaron, "Macheson Stout?"

"...and two ham rolls," he added.

"You will have them," she replied, smiling as she left. He watched as she passed behind the walnut brown bar and pulled down a thick, dark bottle. Into a pint glass she poured the thick ale. Coolly, Aaron stared at her as though she was a deer about to sprint into a virgin forest. Several customers stood at the bar; others talked quietly, as they sipped pints of bitter. She circled and wove her way through them and brought him his drink.

"Here we are," she said. "Your rolls will be a few minutes."

He beckoned her to come closer.

"Can I see you later tonight?"

She thought a moment and nodded with a smile. This young man appealed to her, in part because he was American and thus different from other blokes in this part of England but also, in part, because he was a stranger, someone she could get wild with. No one knew him. His anonymity allowed him liberties with her and, her with him, that she would seldom allow the local blokes. And Aaron was not one to avoid a wild time where he could find it. After all, he was from the States. And he had to do so within the limits of curfew and blackouts. Other limits were too long to list: everything could only be measured in time: how he had left his proud but sad parents in Bayonne; induction into the army; having to wear a uniform at all limited him, he thought. Time and time again he was tempted to go, just leave, to desert, but an ample streak of patriotism tempered such thoughts which were now interrupted as she set two ham rolls on his table.

"I've asked him," she said, gesturing in the direction of the bartender who was drying some pint-sized glasses, "and he says I can go since we close early anyway. I don't want to stay here and drink, Aaron," she added with a curious mixture of pleading and exotic forbiddenness in her voice.

He had finished one roll and was biting into the second one, when Wendy emerged from behind the bar with her coat in hand. She was ready to go. He rose and took her hand as they ventured into the foggy night. Salty coastal breezes pervaded the night air. They made their way down side streets until they reached the edge of town.

"I brought it for us," she said, pulling a candle from her coat pocket.

This caught Aaron by surprise. What did she have in mind? he thought. On they strolled until they came to what looked like it was at one time an alehouse. Wendy assured him she was familiar with it and, taking him by the hand, she led him in. As far as they knew, no one had seen them go in. Darkness enveloped them. A scent of wood and hay emerged in one corner of the structure as the tiny flicker of the candle endowed it with a faint pinkish glow.

"God, you're bold," he said as she grinned broadly.

"I do like some Yanks, especially someone I know." Wendy had seemed somewhat shy before and now she was coming on so strong it almost scared him. She unbuttoned his coat as his heart raced. Aaron was bowled over by her audacity. Her legs felt warm next to his, though her fingertips were cold. After awhile as the loving subsided, she became serious with an almost wistful look on her face.

"You're so young...such a fine man...why another war?" she said.

"There has to be another war because...people love it. Or they're bored and want to be important..." he mused absently even though it was obvious he was becoming annoyed by the insertion of war into their conversation. Though she noticed the disgust in his voice, amazingly she continued:

"When do you have to go?"

"Not too long. I can't talk about it. Not now."

"I will miss you," she said, stroking his jaw line. He smiled pensively but said nothing. The glow of the candle grew more and more faint. At least if it were to go out, they knew where they were in the room. They knew where the door was. Wind now and then whirred through cracks in the wood and stone and an occasional gust spun bits of hay around on the floor. Still this old place was a relief against the night. They kissed again long and longer.

Outside, the fog harbored the military might and determination of those whose turn it was to answer the call to join in the praise of folly. Wars were easy to start: border disputes, trampling ambition, uncreative boredom, insults real or imagined, testosterone overload, purist bigotries, prolonged amnesia, religious fanaticism, visionless glory, power seductions, imperial arrogance, will contests, and the list went on. Yet it was peace that was hard. Waging peace was the most difficult to master since it included mastering hatred, ego, and ignorance. In the distance, in the shell fire night of sea breezes and the muted drone of planes could be heard high above clouds embellished by thick covers of fog.

Their brief time slipped away like birds dissolving in flight. As the wind increased, a window pane rattled like soft tapping fingers in the night. Their candle formed glowing pools at its base, pools that would soon strangle the now-diminishing flame. He stared as the flame's reflection danced on her smooth flesh.

After a long time, he said:

"The candle's going out."

"Don't worry. We can find our way in the dark."

"Still. We had better go. I've got to get back. Besides, you don't have another light."

Reluctantly, very reluctantly, she acknowledged that fact. They zipped and buttoned up and made their way out into the darkness. The wind blew her hair across her face which was still wistful and a little sad.

It was not far to her house; they kissed long on the porch stairs. He told her he would see her again tomorrow night. After such an assurance, and a touching evening, however crude or modest, she went inside. Although he desperately wanted to, he knew he could not see her again. There were too many things to do and think about. Besides, he could not take saying goodbye. It was better this way, he thought. It was only a matter of hours until he would be going to France. He would get to know Omaha Beach intimately in the pivotal invasion of Normandy. He would never see her again. But now, as he rode back to the base, he could barely hear the faint hum of high-altitude planes and distant bombardment. He also knew, in the sea breezes of this war, an armada of fog-enshrouded ships lay ponderous, poised and ready on the restless and brooding Channel. It seemed as though this would be the twilight of the gods.

In spite of this, maybe tomorrow will be sunny, he thought, yes, tomorrow.

The One Hundred Club

Erehwon Manor, once a family residence, rises out of gray morning mists like an ocean liner looms out of a thick fog at sea. Architecturally, it is a masterpiece of Elizabethan and Jacobean design with the excessive ornamentation of the Victorian era in which it was built. It is also the scene of a biannual hunt of the One Hundred Club which provides hunting opportunities for those who have to be at least one hundred years old.

On a Sunday in December and June, they meet in town and drive out to Erehwon with their shotguns and boxes of shells to shoot pheasant. Trees, shrubs, uncut weeds and grasses and hedges of various heights surround the manor. A swamp that was at one time a lake broods on the west side of the property with a statue of a missionary praying in front of it. There is also rumored to be a fountain of youth somewhere on the manor property. When one drinks of its waters, one ceases to get old, becomes healed, and can see at the bottom of the fountain the sacredness of water as portrayed in so many religions and folk tales all the way back to the Rig Veda of ancient India. But none of the hunters has so far found it. Or if one has found it, not one word has been said about it or its restorative properties.

I parked my car in the enclosed bull ring at the front of the manor. As I walked up the steps leading to the cricket field, I began to see some hunters at various parts of the manor grounds. One hunter in gray boots and Sherlock Holmes hat, clomped through some tall weeds at moments stalking as though he heard something about to flush out of the weeds, at others standing up as though listening to the cooing of pigeons in the trees. At one point, I stood behind a tall shrub at the top of the lawn that sloped down to the cricket field below only to be startled by an older man with slumped shoulders and grayish hair and slight sideburn curls, bowed low and said to my surprise: "Dr. Livingstone, I presume." I assured him I was not the famed missionary and explorer. He bowed low as though to beg my pardon and soon disappeared into a nearby thicket. It was not long before I encountered an auburn-haired man with hunting cap and ruddy face who strutted out from behind a tall pillar. "Glad I checked first. Before I fired. I thought you was a pheasant."

"Do I look like a bird?" I said with unfeigned disgust.

"Come to think of it...you don't. Many pardons, Ma'am," he said as he disappeared into a grove of trees and thick underbrush.

To say that I was becoming disgusted, not to mention apprehensive, would be a vast understatement. So far, I had been mistaken for a missionary, a pheasant and even a woman. It did not seem this brief afternoon would be all that pleasant, even if I *were* a pheasant.

I had not proceeded more than twenty-five paces when an old gentleman dressed in blue trousers, gray knit sweater, and checkered cap stepped in front of me. He wore a black patch over one eye. He stooped over and his hands trembled and slightly shook while holding his shotgun that I figured must have weighed two or three pounds.

"S—s—Sonny. P—pardon me, but can you t-tell me where some pheasant are?" He tried to smile, but having only a few teeth, kept his lips closed most of the time.

"They're probably in those woods or out there in the fields," I said, indicating the long, newly-plowed, clod-knotted fields that stretched past the manor gate near a stream that ran under that part of the road that led to the manor.

"I s-see. Thankee Sonny," he said as he suddenly lifted the shotgun to his shoulder and swung the barrel across the horizon and fired. A large pheasant had got away with its life but the praying hands had not. They were chipped, causing some pieces to fall off, and the missionary's nose had been nicked. I decided to tiptoe away while he was looking the other way.

Although I made my way through low-hanging brambles to the statue of the watchful lion that slept at the back of the manor, a bullet zinged by my head. Then another. What to do? The shots stopped.

"You k—k—know somethin, s–s–sonny, I thought you was a lion." Then he laughed hard as though the whole world was laughing with him.

"No, I'm not a lion. You should be more careful. Open your eyes next time."

I left him and kept looking back as I moved away. I did not want to be shot at again. Next to a ramp leading to the back of the manor stood an elderly gent with a head of wavy white hair who looked almost young compared to some of the hunters I had already encountered. It turned out this bloke, whose name was Owyn Benflower, knew most of the hunters who regularly attended these hunting expeditions. He seemed much younger, a relative youngster in this crew. He held his gun pointed downward so it would not harm anyone.

"Who was that?" I asked.

"Oh, that was Nick. He gets a bit wild with a gun in his hands. We have to keep an eye on him."

"I'll say. He almost hit me in the head," I said matter of factly.

"He does get carried away..." Owyn said.

"Around these parts, he goes by the nickname 'Nick the One-Eyed Gunner'"

"Because he has a patch over one eye?"

"Well, he *is* blind in one eye. And should be wearing his glasses for the other."

"Oh, that should improve his marksmanship," I said somewhat sarcastically.

Just then Nick the One-Eyed Gunner began to amble in our direction.

"Here he comes again," I said to Owyn.

"Hey, Nick, take it easy. You scared my friend Jack Russell here. Your bullets nearly hit him. He ducked out of the way, you might say, in the nick of time."

After a low chuckle, Nick said: "S—s—sorry Sonny. So s—s—sorry."

"You need to be after the pheasants. That's what you came here for, Nick. They are probably over past that lawn near the woods," said Owyn, indicating a westerly direction past the cricket field and the elaborately carved tool shed.

"Thankee, Owyn. That you, Owyn?" he said, squinting, as though all he needed in the world was to focus more clearly.

"Yes, it's me, Nick. It's me." Nick gave us both a feeble salute then ambled off, holding his gun across his chest, ostensibly in pursuit of wild pheasant.

"Have a good hunt, Nick," said Owyn.

"How can somebody whose a hundred years old be allowed to hunt?"

"Hey, I'm a hundred and two."

"You are *not*. I don't believe it. You don't look a day over ninety-five." I said.

"I really am. Nick's a hundred and eight."

"Only six years older? He seems much older than you."

"People age at different speeds. They really do."

"You're very clear. You speak well. He can hardly speak clearly."

"Still, it's true. I may be just like that in six years," he said, sad at the thought.

After a pause, he continued:

"But back to your original question. It's a kind of recreation for senior citizens."

"But it's not recreation to be shot at!"

"That's true. This must be your first time."

"No, my second," I said with a measure of disgust.

"You might say it's a kind of occupational therapy," Owyn continued.

"Hmmmph," I grumbled. "Too many things are done in the name of therapy these days," I said.

"We all need a little therapy now and again," remarked Owyn as he continued to scan the manor grounds for other hunters. At most there seemed to be no more than seven hunters in all, one more than the last hunt six months earlier. After a few moments my curiosity got the better of me and finally I asked:

"How *do* you stay so young? You don't look very old at all. Certainly when compared to these other hunters here."

"I'm a retired archaeologist. Taught for over forty years at the local college. Still go on digs for bones, artifacts like jewelry, and bones now and then. But for the most part I'm just enjoying retirement."

"But how *do* you stay so young? And look so young at a hundred and two?"

Owyn thought a moment. Then he surveyed the manor grounds again.

"Well, it's easy to look young when you're surrounded by fossils," he said with a slight smile.

I had to agree. He looked at least ten to fourteen years younger than these hunters out here, especially Nick the One-Eyed Gunner. He discerned from my face that my curiosity had not been satisfied so he continued:

"No, I just stay active. Keep up with the latest fossil finds. And tend to my garden of roses and tulips. Keep them well tended. Go to the Blue Rhino, a pub near where I live. Play a few round of darts with the youngsters. Down some cool brown ale like Macheson Stout or Newcastle-on-Tyne. So it's not just to be around fossils since I am becoming one myself. But to eat some really fine food. That's one of the reasons I come to these hunts."

"Really. That's why I came today. Not to hunt but to have some of that delicious pheasant. Why last time I was here the cook, I think his name is Skip, made a roast pheasant with bacon and garlic that was scrumptious."

"He puts it together, doesn't he? And Shepherd's Pie, especially when he puts a layer of corn between the meat and potato layers with a dash of barbecue sauce. Deeelicious!" crooned Owyn.

"Whether it's beef or lamb curry. Or a salad with potatoes and beetroot with goats cheese, Skip's dishes make you forget you're here for the roast pheasant."

"And don't forget," added Owyn with gusto, "his famous dessert. Custard Pie."

"You're making me hungry," I said.

"And for another dessert, maybe in our spare time, we can look for a fountain of youth that's supposed to be on the property here somewhere but I haven't found it."

"I haven't either. That would be a baptism worth dying for," I said.

"We'll have to keep hunting won't we?"

"Indeed. We sure will."

Just then a flock of pigeons that had burst out from some thick trees were greeted with gunfire. Only one was shot down. Nick's gun had done the deed. Owyn shot his gun into the air to get Nick's attention.

"Hey, Nick! Hey, Nick!" Nick looked over in his direction.

"Did that look like a pheasant?" Reluctantly, Nick shook his head.

"Don't shoot the pigeons, Nick. We're here for pheasant. Remember that."

At that point, I decided to stay inside the manor; it appeared to be too dangerous to be outside with such hunters.

"I think I'll stay in the manor. There's some books in the library."

"I understand. I should stay out here and keep an eye on these guys. You never know what might happen."

"You can say that again," I said as I walked through the large doors leading to the library with its collections of Mutswairo, Shakespeare, Transtromer, Unamuno, Woolf, Swinburne, Arrabal, Goethe, Wordsworth, Pirandello, Lao Tzu, Dostoevsky, Borges, and Keats, movies, TV series and concerts. In a couple hours, the hunt would be over. And the grand feast, well worth waiting for, would begin.

Meditation Interruptus

S tapled to a tree trunk was a hand-painted sign announcing a performance of the music of India and meditational exercises led by prolific author and Zen devotee, Bhaghwan Mysore.

The three stood there reading it.

"We should go," Mark said.

"Yes, let's. I like Mysore anyway," declared Orestes.

Sandy just smiled in her usual bemused way.

The Saturday following they arrived at the university campus and parked near tennis courts as reddish-hued as the clay of north Georgia.

"That's the beauty of the full-lotus position," concluded Mark, "it's the balance and low center of gravity..."

"How do you know so much about it?" asked Orestes.

"Years of practice. And much reading."

Mark was almost boastful about his buoyant interest in Buddhist meditational techniques. He had developed his interest in meditation about four years earlier due to the influence of a friend of his father who was a member of the White Robed Monks of St. Benedict, an order of Dutch Catholic monks that practice Zen sitting or zazen. A student at the university, he was majoring in philosophy and art; his extensive meditational experience had disciplined his mind and made him, so he said, a calmer person. His shoulder-length dark hair floated over his Hawaiian shirt that featured the entire island chain and flutteredslightly in the breeze as he described his favorite subject. Sandy listened carefully; she respected Mark's opinion; for her, this was an area she knew nothing about but was interested in, especially since she had begun dating Orestes.

"The idea is to calm the mind by calming your samsaric thoughts; that is, your everyday thoughts are distractions that prevent you from focusing your life, your being," explained Mark.

"But how do you do that?" asked Orestes.

"Breathing. Focus on breathing...and the point where your nose becomes the focal point where you breathe in and out...You just concentrate your breathing and avoid outside distractions. I think you got the hang of it when we tried it last night. You both were able to shut out the sirens and other sounds of the night. You both did well. You didn't even need ear plugs. That's how some on this odyssey try it."

They passed an S-shaped pond where ducks and geese swam at leisure. An island, shaded by willows weeping, was connected to the land by a redwood arched bridge so people could pass over it and visit the little island where the ducks and geese slept at night. Passing an ivy-covered wall, they came to a large gymnasium where this festival of Indian music and meditation was to take place. They sat down toward the back near a scoreboard. Mats had been placed on the floor to alleviate cramping and discomfort that frequently accompanied sitting in meditational positions. Erotically exotic music by the group called *The Five Skandas* curled like smoke through the rafters: it included the twang of the sitar with its subtle, sensuous vibrations; castanets clicking; and bongo drums with a steady patter of rhythmic fingers calloused by years of playing.

At length, Mysore emerged and sat on a huge pink pillow; he then assumed the full-lotus position. His beard was streaked with silver. His pants were made of silk and fit rather loosely; his shirt billowed at the shoulders yet fitted snug about his wrists. The lights began to dim slowly. His aura remotely resembled that of a maharaja but his simple mode of being resembled that of a Zen monk. Greeting this large audience, he welcomed them to this festival of lights. About three feet in front of Mark and company was a blond girl seated in the full-lotus position with her purse, sweater, and bag of granola cereal next to her. Just at an angle to her was a door that remained ajar for latecomers. Mark assumed the full-lotus position, his thumb and index finger of each hand touching. His breathing deepened; he firmed his spine at a right angle to the floor, and neatly tucked each leg beneath his body for the full effect of a low center of gravity. The night before he had explained the touching of the thumb to the index finger as a symbol of cosmic unity. At times he would raise his hand with his index finger pointed up; he had explained that was gesture of peace of would-be buddhas with all sentient beings. Sandy and Orestes watched him and they, too, assumed the full-lotus position. Sandy was much more used to this position, having tried it more times than had Orestes. But there he was — his blue-trimmed sweatshirt outlining large freckled muscular arms, his Levi's somewhat loose about the waist, his hair a bit shorter and browner than Mark's, his brown eyes adjusting to the subdued light — a portrait of an eager learner in this intoxicating mixture of body-space and time.

The entire gym was soon filled with meditation; the music became softer and more subdued until it finally ceased. Seated in the full-lotus position, Mysore lifted his hand in a gesture of peace, fingers pointed heavenward, his head still, his eyes half-closed, his spine erect, his breathing deep, and began to hum the sacred mantric syllable "OM", itself a symbol of unity, a symbol of harmony of the inner self with the cosmos, a perfect nasal-producing circle. It spread like ripples to the lips of everyone.

A sense of harmony through repeated versions of Ommmmmmm Ommmmmm Ommmmmm Ommmmmmmmm Ommmmmmmmmmm began to pervade the entire gym. Unity began to vibrate from their delicious breathing in this search for the experience of oneness, of the possibility of nirvana itself. As Mark had described to them the previous evening, the deeper the meditation the more relaxed brain activity would become until an indescribable sense of peace permeated one's being.

In his own way, Orestes was becoming quite relaxed, although his legs were beginning to feel uncomfortable. Though seated in the full-lotus position, Sandy also felt some discomfort. Both were glad mats had been provided. A deeper sense of relaxation and harmony began to be felt, as though global harmony were indeed possible, as though a sense of planetary peace were deservedly inevitable.

As mentioned, the door to their right and ahead of them had been left ajar. The angle of outside light, whenever the door was opened, fell right on the blond girl—affectionately dubbed Miss Om—who sat within a few feet of the door. Although some latecomers had used the door already, they had not disturbed this congregation of cosmic unity-producing devotees, this sea of cosmic vibrations, whose meditations on "Om" would produce a peace that passeth all understanding.

Sandy had noticed the German Shepherd whose name, as it turned out, was "Bam" —short for Bamboozle—as he frolicked among the meditators toward where Mysore sat aglow, it seemed, with the relentless rhythm of repeated Ommmmmmmm Ommmmmmmm Ommmmmmmm Ommmmmmm that pervaded the gym. Bam was not one to meditate; in fact, Bam had much more mundane concerns on his canine mind. Far from any feelings of cosmic unity, Bam it seems was emphatically more interested in playtime.

Bam's thoughts, in this fair blossom time, had turned to a kind of lusty playfulness very much in that fashion of divine madness inspiring the animal world, including, of course, that sea of vibrations in which he was now sniffing about.

To this day neither Sandy, Orestes, nor Mark understood what it was about Miss Om's purse that attracted Bam. Perhaps her perfume: it was alarmingly alluring. Maybe it was the purse's soft leather. In any case, Bam got it into his head that Miss Om's purse was something he wanted to play with—and keep.

Once Bam perceived Miss Om's purse in this light, however unsavory it might appear, there was no delay.

45

Bam wanted to frolic. Desperately so. And, after a routine preliminary sniffing around as dogs are wont to do, began trying to tug her purse (and her along with it) out the door.

No one was more surprised than Miss Om. Presumably, her brain waves — alpha ones, to be sure — had slowed parallel with her breathing patterns. So intent were the meditators that hardly anyone even realized Bam's efforts at petty theft. Bam began to growl and tug on the purse strap. Instead of experiencing the "other shore" of nirvana, she now experienced a dog who wanted a detour in which to frolic. Instead of the peace that passeth all understanding, she experienced Bam's natural efforts at a play of his own. At first she tried to be congenial, awakened after a peaceful sleep, and was able to push Bam away. But Bam was as relentless as wind-whipped whitecaps pounding for shore.

Sandy nudged Orestes who saw what was going on. He grinned. He had second thoughts about tapping Mark since Mark was in deep meditation, a dream state.

Again Bam made another assault. He tucked in his tongue as he pulled the purse strap away. Again, she was able to get it away from him. Clearly, Miss Om was becoming exasperated, especially as Bam made another attempt. Fortunately, an herbal essence therapist collared Bam and let him out the door. For a twinkling second there was peace on the eastern front.

Miss Om was grateful; she thanked the therapist who in her essence returned to her mandala-shaped frisbee which marked her spot on a nearby mat.

But Bam was not to be denied. Between Oms Bam's panting and sniffing could still be heard outside the door. He wanted that purse in the worst way. Formidable was Bam's determination; a torrent of doggone attraction spurred him on. Continual sniffing was a distraction that kept both Sandy and Orestes from a deep meditative state. Bam's sniffing also kept both Sandy and Orestes aware of what was about to occur. Just as Miss Om was regaining her composure and resuming her deep breathing, someone opened the door and came in. Another latecomer sat down. It was all the incentive—did Bam ever need an incentive?— and space Bam needed. Seeing his opportunity, he slid through the door. Adjusting his eyes to the gathering's subdued light, he soon found the object of his playful tugs.

Again he sunk his teeth into Miss Om's purse. This time she was able to dislodge them from the purse strap and pushed him away brusquely. Again and again he came back. By this time, Miss Om was so disgusted she thought of leaving. She tried swearing at Bam but he was not deterred. So determined was he that he actually managed to knock her out of the full-lotus position. This began to attract the notice of several others who were increasingly caught up in the commotion. At length her swearing grew louder, even to the point of referring to Bam as a "son of a bitch." Now she was taking swings at Bam.

First a right cross to the upper torso stunned him. Then a sweeping motion with her arm rolled him over on his side. In a flash, he had the purse again. More punches. Now karate chops. More swearing. Miss Om was exasperation itself. Forget nirvana! Forget peace! Forget cosmic unity! Not today! Bam was on the loose!

All the while Mark was in deep meditation, undeterred by all the distractions. Neither Orestes nor Sandy bothered to disturb him, even if they could. He was in another world; one might say he was a thousand lives away.

After several more forays, and after Miss Om was thoroughly disgusted because her alpha waves had been distracted by Bam's resurgent efforts at petty theft, this time a primal scream therapist and a tarot card-sex therapist came to her rescue. Bam was thrown out the door. The primal scream therapist suggested she make a primal scream to relieve her stress; Miss Om told her she was in no mood to assume a fetal position to do so.

Sandy and Orestes grinned at all this. The chorus of Ommmmmmm Ommmmmmm Ommmmmmm Ommmmmm continued as though nothing had happened. Mysore and company were tranquil and

47

thoroughly concentrated on the relentless repetition of Ommmmmmm Ommmmmmmmm.

Miss Om gathered her sweater and now partially-torn purse strap and noticed that in all of his pawings Bam had put a hole in her bag of granola. This only added to her misery. Saving what granola she could, she left this platonic cavern. Fortunately, she left by an exit on the opposite side of the gym. It was worth the effort. There is no telling what would have happened had she gone out the same door where Bam was still sniffing around. Her purse, with all its scents, would have been chewed to shreds. As it was, he remained there sniffing for quite awhile.

They never saw Miss Om again, and, as they left campus, wondered if she had ever found any kind of peace. As for Bam, he was not sniffing too long at the gym door; nor was this pooch waiting with anticipation for some unwitting latecomer. He continued his search for play and frolic, since every distraction has its attractions, in another light.

The Incident at Zeno's Hideaway

O ur private lives, later or sooner, may become an open book. Take this diary, for instance:

1981
page 14

Gabe (he does not like to be called Gabriel) told me he wants out of his marriage. He's only staying in it for the sake of his children. He says he has an obligation to stay with his wife. But we *will* be married soon. You'll see. I have that kind of effect on him. I can be exceptionally persuasive. Besides, staying in a marriage for the sake of his children is not a good reason. It just makes Gabe miserable. I wonder if Penelope feels the same way. I doubt it. Gabe is quite a mover and shaker; the glitter, the powerful all get to me. I have never been around someone like that before.

page 29

Gabe is restless; he's tired of making love on the sly. I've enjoyed being with him. He opens me like a flower. Penelope must be a bore or a witch. She's so demanding on him. Gabe is so giving; my new diamond stick pin is so compelling. I just know we'll be getting married. Last week he promised: "We will get engaged soon." But he balks at the talk of marriage. I just know we'll be getting married.

1984
page 69

Gabe says I look beautiful in my new bikini and pearl necklace he gave me for my twenty-eighth birthday. So far, his wife does not suspect anything. According to Gabe, Penny is so boring he can hardly stand it. He has to move his family because he is being transferred to California by his company. I plan to follow him. I can't conceive of life without him. My friend Lilith says I am crazy for getting involved with an older married man in the first place. "You will end up a broken heart," she tells me over and over. She does admit Gabe is indeed handsome. He becomes more handsome with each of the gifts he brings to our love. What more could a woman want?

1987
page 101

In three years I have seen Gabe only five times. I'm now thirty-two; my biological clock is ticking away. I cherish the diamond earrings he gave me for our sixth anniversary. I've never been so in love and in so much pain at the same time. Love can scar beyond recognition. To hold him even if for only a day...I really want to be married. We would have a wonderful life together. If only Penelope would divorce him or just leave. She stands between me and the one I love. Why would she want to stay around anyway? Gabe told me their marriage was over long ago. She's so demanding. Nags him all the time...about everything. No wonder he wants out.

1989
page 192

Listening to the song "Diamonds and Rust": Love that song. My life seems adrift. I have seen Gabe only five times in the last year. He keeps closer to his family. They even go on vacations together. I'm in California; I don't know many people and the ones at work are only work friends. And they always seem to be going to wine and cheese tastings. You'd think they'd be drunk or at least high most of the time. Some of them are. I don't do much but sit by the phone. Gabe does not return my calls. Yet I sit by the phone, hoping and hoping. So lonely. Can it be that love can turn into its opposite? I don't want to think about it. The diamond necklace he gave me the last time we were together is gorgeous. I just love diamonds. I thought by now we would be married. But that...is more and more a mirage.

page 218

My job now requires that I occasionally fly out of state. I leave word with Gabe and hope Penelope does not have access to his private phone. He does not return my calls. Maybe she knows and erases my messages! That witch! She stands between me and the one I love. That other day I was in town and I swear I saw a woman who looks just like my friend Lilith. I should have gone over and at least introduced myself. But then I thought: "What if it *is* her? What would she be doing out here in California? I called her number that night; it has been disconnected. She's never approved of my pursuit of Gabe. She used to say: "He will nail you. You'll never forgive yourself."

1990
page 232

I am thirty-five and counting. Gabe gave me a diamond "engagement" ring. The word "engagement" does not ring too well with me. We've been lovers too long. I still want a family. He always changes the subject. He says: "As I've told you before, Chance, I have an obligation to my family. Please try to understand that." He's so cute and sincere. I love the way his smile tilts in the corner of his mouth. To me, he's a prince of this world.

1993
page 293

I am now thirty-eight. Time is running out. I want a family with Gabe so badly. But he changes the subject whenever I mention commitment and marriage. In the last three years I have been with him four times. Both of his kids are in college. At times my anger is on the breaking point. At times I hate him. Once I became desperate. I called him at home. Penelope answered the phone. I just hung up. I've done that dozens of times over the past two years. One moment my love is sustained; the next I hate him for all the delays. I have let him put my life on hold. I miss talking with Lilith. The letters to her always return. She has no forwarding address.

1995
page 347

Any hopes of marrying Gabe have vanished. He is always gone. He sure is not at home. I did something I never thought I would do. I refused to accept his diamond bracelet. I told him I would gladly accept it if we talked about our future together. He got angry and slapped me hard. I could not believe he slapped me. His hand left its outline on my face. This is the love of my life and he slapped me. I called in sick at work; I did not want anyone to see the bruise on my face. Though I love him still, I am beginning to see what I did not want to see all along.

1996
page 403

Gabe has not returned my calls in several weeks. Finally I called his home—a desperate move since he has always warned me not to call him at home. Penelope answered. I said: "Is Gabriel there?" A long silence. "You must be Lilith," she said. I swallowed hard. "Lilith?" She continued: "Or is it Lashika this time?" I hung up. Stunned. Lilith? My friend Lilith? I sat there like a statue.

Licked my lips; my breathing became inconsolable. That was all. I saw my life of waiting fly up like flames. Who is Lashika? Where did she come from?

page 444

Out of desperation or habit, I called Gabe's home. Maybe Penelope would blurt out something about Lilith. She answered the phone: "Is Gabe there?" I said muffling my voice. A long silence. "Who is this? Lashika?" Undeterred, I repeated: "Is Gabe there?" After a moment of silence, she said: "No, he's not here. He's probably with his personal secretary. He just hasn't been the same since his surgery." Stunned, I said: "Surgery?" "Yes, he had a vasectomy. Seems he needs to prove himself now more than ever. Like he's not himself anymore. Well, whoever you are, you're the fool." Then she hung up. I sat back, dazed.

1999
page 513

I have given up hope of marriage and a family. When I brought up the subject the other day, Gabe belted me. It was like the previous times I called his home. It hurts to discover your love is not who he appears to be. He also denied having a vasectomy. He said that was how Penelope handled his absences. He denied knowing anyone named Lilith. He also denied knowing anyone named Lashika. Yet I found out Lashika is his personal secretary. She must be good at taking dictation. She recently accompanied him on the company jet to Kansas City on business. That much I was able to find out. Lies, lies, and more lies. I believe Lilith and Lashika are his playthings. I don't know how Penelope puts up with it. A saint she must be. Next thing you know he'll run for public office where half-truths are doubly essential.

2000
page 666

I have taken up a new sport—deer hunting. I want to be able to nail a deer at two hundred yards. Gale Mafisto, my coach at the rifle range, always compliments me. He says my accuracy is rare, especially among women. I am waiting for hunting season to open. Then I'll have my license. Penelope still stands between me and the one I love. My letters to Lilith still return with no forwarding address. I still call Gabe mostly out of habit. On weekends I have been able to follow him in my car. Last Saturday he and a woman left a bar and went to a small hotel called *The Sleeping Stallion*. I had never seen her before but she *was* wearing diamonds. I began to swear under my breath. I feel so used, so angry, so bitter.

2001
page 700

My therapist is terribly helpful.

"Tell me how all this happened," she said one day.

"I've told the police everything. My lawyer. She did the best she could defending me. Even on appeal."

"Tell *me* then." Because she is so helpful, I decided to tell her.

"I had been hit often enough I could not do my job. There were times I just wanted to go back home. But I had none. My father abandoned the family when I was six. Mom died when I was nine. I lived with assorted relatives after that but was not really close to anyone. Then I lost my job. I could not keep pretending. Makeup only goes so far. My jaw was swollen. Gabe was no longer interested. He had found someone new, although occasionally he still gave me gifts such as a sapphire stick pin. I went and pawned it. I was between jobs. Living in limbo."

"Go on."

"One day I called him again–at home. All hell broke loose. He came by my place, broke down the door, and knocked me silly."

"But why did you continue to call? You knew he didn't want that."

"It was habit. With that many years invested. I had given up everything: marriage, family."

"But the warning signs were there all along. You could have cut your losses and walked away.You think you were dazzled by all the attention, the gifts?"

I nodded. "And I was in love."

"You thought you were in love. Love dies on a one-way dead end street."

page 731

We began with my therapist—Mary is her name—listening to my complaints about prison food and the way the guards treat us women. We are treated like swine. She asked about the time I decided to take things into my own hands. It is hard for me to talk about it. It seems that's all I have been doing the last few years.

"As I told you, I began lessons at a rifle range. Accuracy was what I wanted—and got. One afternoon Gabe was abusive on the phone, cussed me out, told me never to call again. Suddenly that was it. Hate rose in me, resentment for all the years of abuse...the broken dreams...I went to get my rifle. I wanted to show him, to get back at him. He thought of me as merely ungrateful for all the times and gifts. I drove out to where he usually went, it was a large park, the one where, set off by itself, a couple of miles away. Zeno's Paradox is...it's better known as Zeno's Hideaway."

"Go on," she said.

"He was standing there waiting...as if waiting for someone. I did not care who. Nor was I gonna wait to find out. I lay flat, got him in my sight, and pulled the trigger. I missed him. He had bent down to get his keys. The bullet landed on the other side of him. He dove under a table as I kept shooting. Then I heard someone cry out. The cry distracted me. Quickly he dashed to his car and drove off. Curious, I checked out the source of the cry. I did not want anyone innocent to be hurt. You know, an innocent bystander. I ran over to where the cry came from. At first there was no sign of anyone."

"Go on," said Mary.

"There she was: Lilith. One of the bullets hit her. And she was dead. I was horrified. There were bruises on her face too. I felt so sad, so betrayed. I ran, got in the car, and in a few minutes caught up with him. He was also responsible for my friend's death."

"But it was one of your bullets that killed *her*…right?" she interjected. I nodded sadly.

"He drove to Zeno's Hideaway. He must have known I could catch up with him on the open road. But Zeno's was the most likely place for him to hide. You know about Zeno's?"

"No, refresh my memory. Is that the place where motion does not exist or at least slows down?"

"Yes. It's named after the philosopher Zeno of Elea's Paradox. It's a thick forest that resists and sometimes stops motion. Sometimes it is called Zeno's Paradox."

"Oh, yes. Zeno's Paradox: for anything to go from point A to point B, A would first have to go one half the distance and then one half of that distance and so on. Pretty soon the space gets smaller and smaller so that you can't go from point A to point B. In any case, motion slows down in that thick grove; it is as if the builders *wanted* to make Zeno's Paradox *come true*."

I am amazed how informed Mary is — even in philosophy which can be therapeutic.

"He drove into the driveway leading to Zeno's Hideaway, got out, and once inside the grove disappeared. Parking the car, I followed him. I watched for any slight movement which would tell me where he was. Minutes took forever. Finally there was a detectable movement. Carefully I took aim and fired. The bullet traveled to the edge and, once inside, slowed then stopped in midair. I could see it spinning, suspended and spinning. Then it fell harmlessly to the ground. It took my breath away. I suddenly felt helpless. You don't have to go in far. In fact, it's best if you don't because you get caught up in a more powerful suspended motion."

"Isn't the Paradox shaped like a heart?"

"Yes, you stop at the center of the heart. That is also where time stops. You move faster around the edges. He must have known that because he was only a few feet, if that far, inside."

"He had called someone on his phone. And he waited. I did not know whether he had called the cops or what. It was so frustrating. I didn't want to go into Zeno's just because he might discover me and escape. So I reloaded and waited. Sooner or later, he would have to come out. Shadows of twilight were already deepening. I bet he would try to crawl out and make a run for it. So I waited and waited."

"Go on," said Mary.

" It wasn't long before a car pulled in the long driveway to Zeno's. Hiding behind some shrubs, I could see the car parked next to Gabe's. Guess who steps out but Lashika, another one of his playthings! I did not know what was going to happen so I made sure my rifle was loaded and aimed at Gabe's car. He would have to make a run for it. Curiously, Lashika stood by the car, waiting. She did not even start for the Hideaway. She just stood there, looking around. Then she walked around Gabe's car, stopped for a moment, and gazed all around. She was dressed fit to kill. Something was about to explode. Tension thickened the air. Dusk was beginning to roll in. Next thing I knew there was a rustle near the edge of Zeno's near the bottom of the heart. Suddenly Gabe shot out, running as fast as the wind. But my accuracy was perfect. I had shot a dear at two hundred yards. Shot that dead deer dead."

"Then what happened?"

"He fell just in front of Lashika. Then I heard a second shot. She pulled Gabe to one side, out of my sight. Then, of all things, she started shooting at me! I crawled to the edge of Zeno's just inside the grove."

"A paradox is a blessed refuge sometimes, isn't it?" observed Mary.

"You're telling me. Suddenly I felt I could survive, that her bullets could not reach me. It was weird. Everything slowed down. A strange feeling splashed over me like

I was a stranger in a stranger paradox. She fired again. Above me I could hear a bullet; I looked up and it was suspended, spinning and spinning. Then it dropped harmlessly to the ground a few feet away. She knew where I was. It was tempted to venture further into this paradox. I thought she might find me. I listened hard but heard nothing. Then, to my complete surprise, I heard sirens in the distance. Gabe *had* called the cops. I did not know if he had called Lashika. Maybe she had come to hunt him down herself. Holding my breath, I waited to see if she was going to take refuge in Zeno's or try to escape. Paradox *can* be a trap, you know. Sure enough, Lashika got in her car and sped off. The sirens were coming closer. I did not want to stay here at all. Crawling to the edge, I did not see anyone in the driveway. As I was desperately trying to dislodge myself from Zeno's, the cops were already in the driveway. It was too late! I crawled back in. Maybe they would not find me. Several squad cars pulled in. I watched as they discovered Gabe's body and called for paramedics and police backup. I was trapped. It was just a matter of when I would have to move. Yet here motion was slowed down to almost nothing. Police dogs, the German Shepherds, sniffed me out. Cops soon surrounded Zeno's. There was no way out. Sometimes I feel like a coward. Surrendering to them. And then seeing those headlines the next day: *Executive Gabriel Love Killed In Ambush Near Zeno's Hideaway; former mistress captured...* But...here I am."

Mary was silent for awhile.

"You still have time to do."

"I've wasted my life."

"You haven't wasted your life. If you have not learned from this, maybe you have...We'll get together again soon. In the meantime, here's a thought you can take with you."

Again she gave me her calling card on which was printed:

Mary Amida, Ph.D., D.D.
Reality Therapy and East-West Counseling

On the other side was a typed-in quote:

> As with the depths of a diamond,
> the interior is twice as important as the surface.
> There are people who are all facade...
> -*Baltasar Gracian*

Over the years I have learned to accept as well as to give other kinds of gifts. They are what matter. Who knows, despite the guilt and the anger, maybe I can find my way out of almost any paradox.

Music City Skyline

After years of reading it in English, I wanted to learn Chinese so I could translate the *Tao Te Ching* of Lao Tzu. Being a lover of nature, I grew to love the gentle ways of the "Old Master" Lao Tzu who had written this little lovely book of five hundred characters during the Chou Dynasty. So I enrolled in a course in Chinese at Vanderbilt University. It was taught by a professor named Dr. Bo Hamilton. There were eighteen students in the class, including me, most of which were not Chinese. There was Brad Southwell from Lithonia, Georgia who was a political science graduate student from Georgia Southern and who was working on a master's degree public administration. Another was Gweneth Yuen from Alpena, Michigan, who was also a graduate student in library science; she had finished a degree in humanities and religious studies at the University of Vermont in Burlington. Abra Kapoor was a sophomore English and philosophy major from Manchester, Tennessee. Scott Harrell was a health science and sociology major from Napa, California. We formed a small circle just by sitting next to each other in Dr. Hamilton's class. In the days and weeks that followed, we got to know each other pretty well since we had to go to the language lab to review each chapter in our book of Chinese grammar. It was not only hearing the language of each character that was a challenge. Unlike an alphabet-based language, Chinese was totally different. One stroke of a character could mean a totally different word. In addition, this language basically had four tones: high, low, rising, and falling. Another feature that stood out about this language was it was monosyllabic, not polysyllabic like so many other languages are. And it was how it was said and in what context it was said. Some words were combinations of characters such as dungsyi (which is a combination of east and west) meaning everything, all that there is.

One day as Scott and Abra were coming out of the language lab, Gweneth and I who were headed in their direction, stopped to say hello. In addition, she mentioned there was an eight week class in Chinese calligraphy which was to start the following Monday.

"Yes, let's take it," said Scott.

"Let me see if I can do it, given my schedule," replied Abra. Gweneth and I had already signed up. They needed at least ten students for the class to go. Gweneth mentioned she would call Brad and anyone else she knew that might be interested. As it turned out, we found the ten students needed and the class was a success, given that it was the first time it was offered. It was taught by Mrs. Li Sun who worked closely with Dr. Hamilton and the rest of the staff. They both advocated the importance of Chinese and Asian culture generally since Korean and Japanese were also taught as part of an overall educational experience.

As the days and weeks went by, Scott and Abra often went to the language lab together. After an hour of listening to tapes of vocabulary and conversations in Chinese, they would have lunch together. One day while eating some grits and finishing her slice of pecan pie, Abra asked Scott who had finished his lunch of steamed veggies and cornbread, if he liked the new course in calligraphy.

"I love it," he replied. "I did not know it was so intricate with each character telling a story in the word itself."

"Isn't that something," commented Abra. "It shows how language mirrors a people's history. I like Mrs. Sun too. She obviously loves what she does and how each character has a story."

I, too, came in that day to the Kegger Shack. I had learned to really enjoy steamed veggies and cornbread and an ice-cold soda. Invited to sit with them, we talked briefly about a family visit by Abra's folks the next weekend. But the real focus of our conversation was Mrs.

Sun's course. We all agreed that the characters we were learning had more than just conveying information to say. The story and history of the Chinese people were truly amazing. I thought this was fascinating: the character of a country is formed by realizing that among humans each person had to defend his own land with weapons in a well-defined boundary. That's the character pronounced gwō with a long ō. In addition, since China, like many countries or civilizations, assumed they were the center of the world, a kind of ethnocentrism, they were called the middle kingdom. The character for middle was simply a small rectangle lengthwise and to emphasize its being the middle kingdom, a vertical stroke right down the middle emphasized the middle kingdom pronounced jūng with a long ū. So the word for China became Jūnggwō.

中國

As the days went by, Gweneth and I noticed that a romance was beginning to blossom between Scott and Abra; soon Brad, who always seemed to be busy with government and policy concerns, began to notice as well. It was not a situation that was all that demonstrative in terms of love; they were not kissing or hugging, at least not publicly, but it was just a quiet flowing together not just in the language lab but you could see them together in the library, having lunch together, walking across campus together; it was like the red bud trees were secretly already in bloom.

The following week I spent seven hours in the language lab, repeating one sentence after another in Chinese and answering questions based on conversations that were played over and over. Gradually, we all began to recognize characters after having them repeatedly drilled in our heads. It was becoming a language of our own. In our calligraphy class, one of the characters we learned to create by a brush stroke was the character for love. This was so appropriate, especially in light of the romance between Scott and Abra.

The character for love was formed by recognizing that cloudlike vapor rising up from the earth resembles the human breath. Another form of this character looks like three puffs of air breathed into some kind of thing. What gives breath to the heart in a slow, gracious motion is love. For the ancient Chinese, the heart was the seat of the mind since thought as well as feeling develop in the heart. The Chinese character for a heart indicates three beats above a curved hook-shaped character.

愛

As the days and weeks of the semester wore on, the class soon became acquainted with Dr. Hamilton's dog, Sammy who was a terrier-beagle mix and somewhat smaller than a beagle. His nose was more pointed than squared like most beagles and his tail, which had nerve damage when a wind gust blew a door shut when he was a puppy, swung out to the left as he walked or ran. It was not surprising that he understood commands in the four languages in which Dr. Hamilton was particularly fluent, namely Japanese, Chinese, Spanish, and Arabic. He was a smart dog and Dr. Hamilton had him well trained thanks to a stint at obedience school. His diet was the best money could buy, including venison and wild boar, not to mention high protein chicken and beef along with assorted vegetable flavors. The lovely thing about Sammy was his disposition; he was gentle and friendly, not just with grown-ups but with little kids as well.

Soon Mrs. Sun introduced the class to a character I was especially interested in, namely the Tao. What on earth did it mean? Isn't that character central in the *Tao Te Ching* (dow-day-jing) by Lao Tzu? Yes, it is. Sometimes the Tao was seen as a metaphysical principle that, when written or spoken, was not or no longer the Tao. "The Tao that can said is not the eternal Tao…"

As a character, Mrs. Sun pointed out that feet running or stopping, in ancient China, meant an "advance," going in a certain way or direction. Then a head with two tufts of hair right on top was how the head was drawn. With the feet and head advancing or going in the same direction, that was the path, the way, or simply called the Tao. So, that was it, the Tao meant your head and your feet were going in the same directions; that was to flow as life flows, to go with the flow, as rivers flow to the sea. The power of that flow stemmed from action that was natural and not forced (wu-wei) and its power, soft like water, could eventually cut through rock.

道

A few weeks later, they had another midterm exam. During the exam, Scott became distracted while he was looking around the room, even at the ceiling, trying to think of the character to fill in the blanks, thus showing he was correctly reading the sentence in Chinese.

Soon his eyes landed on Sammy who was lying on the floor with his paws stretched out before him in a prone position. Scott began whispering to Sammy and this came to Dr. Hamilton's attention. He did not want his dog, however cute and otherwise well-behaved, to become a distraction for his students. Sammy soon looked over at him. Professor Hamilton spoke to him in Chinese: ni dzou ba! This command means: "how about you leave the room." At that point, Sammy got up and went out the door the professor was holding open for him. That did the trick. Students returned their focus to their exams with no further distractions.

Final exams were about two weeks away. They always arrived around the bend faster than any students wanted. But they were coming up. The week prior to finals week, the class was invited to come to Dr. Hamilton's house for the afternoon for a kind of end of the semester party. I drove with Mrs. Sun. Four others decided to ride together in Brad's car, each of them chipping in for some gas money. Brad's car was an old station wagon his folks had given him for his twenty-first birthday. After all, he had achieved good grades at Georgia Southern and had been admitted to Vanderbilt which was considered the "Harvard of the South" for his master's degree.

The day for the party finally arrived. It was an unusually warm, sunny day for December. As they drove up a long driveway, they noticed how upward they were driving so that soon the city was off in the distance below. They came to a driveway that formed a circle around a center garden of beautifully-arranged and well-pruned roses, daffodils, and orchids. A man appeared in a white suit who directed them to a place to park off to one side. Other students from the class were already there since there were five other cars already parked on the same side. Mrs. Sun and I arrived much earlier.

As they moved toward the front door, they could not help but notice a beautiful swimming pool with the water being filtered by a hose that snaked gently back and forth around the pool. On each corner of the pool were statues of what looked like Greek and Roman gods and goddesses. A statue of Zeus, the chief god of the pantheon of divinities on Mount Olympus was on one end. Venus, the goddess of love in the ancient Roman religion, stood at another end. A statue of Athena, the Greek goddess of wisdom, art, commerce and war, stood at another end. And finally, the Greek god Apollo, god of music, poetry, and medicine, stood at the other end.

Another man in a white suit opened the front door and invited us in. They were amazed at an exquisitely beautiful interior with prints in frames from some of the master artists of world art. Over the fireplace was a picture of "Le Moulin de la Galette" by the Impressionist Auguste Renoir. Next to a set of book shelves was a picture titled "A Sunday Afternoon on the Island of La Grande Jatte" by the Post-Impressionist Georges Seurat. Mrs. Sun was already there gazing at the lovely paintings. Soon Dr. Hamilton's wife, Edith, came out to meet the students as did his nineteen year old daughter Mulan. In the next room was a familiar face, namely Sammy who was sprawled on a deep red rug. The dining room had a variety of foods on it, namely everything from pepperoni, sausage, olive, Hawaiian pineapple, and Canadian bacon combination pizza to Chinese food such as broccoli beef, barbecue chicken chow mein, to sweet and sour pork and to sandwich ingredients such as roast beef, cheese, and finally to garlic bread and San Francisco sourdough bread. A variety of soft drinks, sparkling water, and pure mountain water was served by the man in the white suit on a silver platter as he circled among the students who were, not surprisingly, invariably hungry. Students could eat inside the home or sit out on a patio and soak up the sun. As they ate and talked, they could not help but notice a long building that extended along the property. Maybe it was Brad or possibly Scott who asked Dr. Hamilton what it was. He went over and pressed a button just inside the front door to the house. Doors to each rose, revealing cars in each garage. Brad was quite curious; it turned out to be a seven car garage. And these were not any ordinary cars. It turned out Dr. Hamilton was a passionate fan of antique cars. Brad got up and went to the first garage. It turns out Brad was also a fan of antique cars from Rolls Royces to Bentleys.

"And what is this," he asked Dr. Hamilton, pointing to the first garage.

"A 1949 MG," said Dr. Hamilton proudly.

"I like the blue color," commented Brad. Soon Scott and Abra came over. They too were impressed.

"Wow, a Duesenberg!" exclaimed Brad. "My parents used to talk about that one!"

"Yes, that's a 1937 model," commented Dr. Hamilton.

"I sure like the Corvette. I wouldn't mind driving that around," remarked Scott as he smiled at Abra who also seemed tantalized by the 1967 red convertible.

"And this one?" I asked.

"A 1966 Ferrari," commented Dr. Hamilton proudly. "In my dreams I'd love to drive it in the Daytona 500." Brad just smiled as did Scott and Abra.

"But the one I drive the most is the least expensive to drive, this 2003 Honda Accord."

"I would imagine it would cost a lot to drive these others, especially the Kissel Gold Bug Speedster. But you would have to take them out for a spin just to make sure they're in good running condition."

"Exactly. Exactly," said Dr. Hamilton, acknowledging the limits of owning antique cars.

"That's quite a collection," remarked Brad. "Exquisite."

"Thank you, Brad. I have to agree," said Dr. Hamilton, "it's a love I have had for a long time."

"Understandably. As have I...I sure can understand that."

Not long after the shadows began to get longer as sunset approached and it was time for the party to be over. Everyone bid thanks and goodbye to Dr. Hamilton and his family. It had been quite an adventure and an eye-opening one at that. As Brad, Gweneth, Scott and Abra drove down the long, winding driveway so that the lights of Nashville began to outline the city and its prominent buildings such as the Grand Ole Opry, the Capital building and the stadium where the Tennessee Titans play their games, their thoughts turned to what they had seen at Dr. Hamilton's home.

"Could you believe that place?" asked Scott.

"I saw it with my own eyes," said Abra.

"At first I thought Vanderbilt must pay extremely well," commented Brad.

"When I went inside to get some more food, I got to talking with Mrs. Sun and I point blank asked her what about all this luxury. I turns out that Dr. Hamilton is an heir to a lumber and paper fortune," said Gweneth.

"No wonder," said Scott.

"Yet, if he's that rich, why would he go to school to earn a doctorate when he could have spent his days by the pool drinking hot toddies and sipping mint juleps."

"I respect him for that," said Brad. "You're right he could have done that and simply enjoyed his wealth."

"Yet," according to Mrs. Sun, "he went to Vanderbilt, Princeton, and earned his doctorate at Stanford and studied all these languages."

"That's quite impressive. I respect him for that," repeated Brad.

The students came back the following week and took their exams, having temporarily forgotten all they had experienced at Dr. Hamilton's home. Yet I did not. It was a memory of that I will keep for as long as I live. By the way, I found translating the *Tao Te Ching* to be quite a challenge, even after three years of studying the language. Parts of it were straight forward and somewhat easy to literally translate. Then there were other parts of it that lost me. It was very much like venturing into a thicket in which one can get lost. From other translations and even transliterations, the *Tao Te Ching* is a formidable undertaking regardless of how clear a translator tries to make it.

The Reunion

"That son of a bitch," complained Daryl. "Can you imagine him wanting to escort me anytime anywhere."

"Who is him?" asked her husband Def.

"A classmate of mine. From high school."

"Why would he want to escort you anytime anywhere?"

"He was my escort in the 12th grade when I was a candidate for Halloween queen."

"You can sure be naïve at times, Def."

"He was being obnoxious and coming on to me. My honor has been offended. It was at our high school luncheon where many of us girls have put on a lot of weight. Girls in high school were thin but now some of them weigh over three hundred pounds."

"I have to defend the Sysie family honor, honey. What can I do to get back at this guy?"

"Let me think about it for awhile."

She sits comfortably in front of the TV and turns the volume down.

"The best part of the trip was to see my first great granddaughter. She's so cute and a darling smile. Only three months old and what a dear."

Later that evening, she texted her long-time friends and classmates, Tim Zoyle and Conrad Lamm:

"We've been friends since we all attended Saint Clements Catholic School through the eighth grade. I need your help now. It was bad enough Dr. Dawson has more education than all of us put together. But now he has offended my honor by saying he would escort me anytime, anywhere. Remember he was my escort for

Halloween queen in the 12th grade. I felt he was coming on to me."

"What can I do to help?" asked Tim. "You and Con come up with something. I know he was proud of all the books he's written when interviewed on *Valley Interviews*."

"When we saw that, it re-ignited my jealousy that I have had toward him through the years. Con and I discussed it and we decided we should do something to his books at the Napa County library."

"Now you're talking," enthused Daryl. "I'll see if I can come up with something that Deft can do to harm him in D.C. Give hugs and love to your families," closed Daryl.

A week later Tim and Con met in Napa and drove over to the library on Coombs Street.

"I'll go and find out where his books are in the library. You can come in and browse." Tim and Con went into the foyer of a busy downtown library just down the street from the courthouse and police department.

Minutes later Con came by and motioned for them to go. Once in the car, Con pulled out of his coat a copy of Kent Dawson's books *Red Orchids and Daffodils* and *Sailing Above the Clouds*. This brought a smile to the ever-envious lips of Tim Zoyle whose jealousy dated from the time he was eight years old playing for the Spiders fly league baseball team when he complained to the coach that Dawson was always chosen to be pitcher. The coach replied: "He's a better pitcher and I want the best pitcher on the mound."

"I don't believe you," gushed Tim. "Nobody saw you? "It was easy pickins, not even a security camera back in the stacks," said Con.

"How come you're so good at theft?"

"You have to be pretty stealthy," replied Con. "I found out how good I was when I could steal cigarettes from the Eastwood market and the guy never even knew they were gone."

"What kind of cigarettes?"

"Ah, it was French name. I'd take them back and meet Kent in the eucalyptus tree at the entrance to his home and we'd smoke them and then say 'I flip over Elvis' and toss the butts to the road below."

"Wow, that's quite a feat," said Tim.

"So it would be nice to steal all of Kent's books. That's one way to get back at him for offending Daryl's dignity since she is the ring leader of the Saint Clements Connection."

"That's quite a task. You think it can be done."

"Sure. We can come back and steal one or two at a time till they're all gone."

"That'll teach him a lesson. He won't believe his eyes when he sees they're all gone."

"You're a great thief, Con, that's all I can say. I'm glad we're on the same side."

***

"Don't you know anyone at the copyright office?" asked Daryl. "I mean you work right there."

"I'll go down there and talk to an acquaintance of mine. Maybe she can come up with something."

A few days later at the cafeteria, Def nodded at one acquaintance, Cruisin, who worked at the copyright office."

"Mind if I join you," asked Def.

"Not at all," replied Cruisin, an attractive black woman whose hubby left her for a younger white woman.

They brought their cafeteria trays of food that was available with quite a variety from mashed potatoes, gravy, chicken and roast beef, fruit and vegetables, and salads with many dressings to choose from.

After Deft told her about the situation with Kent, Cruisen said: "Maybe I could email him and apologize for taking so long to get back to him as about a particular book that we need to know which of his works are in the public domain and those which are not."

"Any book in mind?" asked Cruizin.

"My wife wants to try *Twenty Short Stories*."

"Okay, we'll try that. Maybe he'll take the bait. I'll give him twenty days to comply or he'll have to pay the copyright fee of $85 all over again."

After that, their conversation turned to more mundane topics and general amounts of small talk.

That evening Def told Daryl about the plan and she was pleased but still not satisfied; the scheme was not hurtful enough since she really hated Kent with a deep vein of viciousness.

"There's got to be something else we can do," she said. "I'm holding you responsible for coming up with something that will castrate that bastard."

"I'll certainly try," replied Def.

***

Meanwhile Kent received the email Cruizin had described. He was puzzled about the request but, not knowing Daryl and Def were behind the scheme, assumed it was legitimate. What puzzled him was his books had been copyrighted beginning with his doctoral thesis years before and nothing had been said. No one had written him to determine which of the articles included in the bibliography had been in the public domain or were only privately printed and therefore accessible only to a few scholars and members of the public.

Kent spent the next few weeks trying to remember where which stories had been published or reprinted. Once he finished, and after several rejections by Cruizin that his replies were not correct, he got it right. Cruizin was satisfied and promised to send him by regular mail a copy of his registered copyright which she eventually did.

***

A week later, Def dropped by Cruizin's office since they were having lunch together. Because it was such a nice day outside, they decided to grab a table at a Georgetown restaurant.

"I have good news for you," began Cruizin. "He thought it was a legitimate request and has done all I asked for all twenty stories."

"Fantastic," declared Def. "Can't wait to tell my wife. This calls for a celebration. Let me pay for your lunch."

"Thank you," said Cruizin, who was surprised when Def gave her a kiss. She had not been kissed by a white man before. "I can't wait for the next book. Has your wife picked out one?"

"What's that?" asked Def who was focused on the kiss.

Unbeknownst to them, one of Kent's relatives had taken their picture as they kissed and sent a copy of it to Daryl.

"Yes, uh, yes, it is one we received from Tim and Con in California. Kent's *Collected Poems 1965-1985* and the acknowledgements page is loaded with journals and reviews—at least two hundred—that are in the public domain. It will take him awhile to do that same task for you. One of our classmates Con stole it from the Napa County library and sent the acknowledgements by email."

That night he told Daryl about what happened with Cruizin and the twenty stories.

"How wonderful!" cried Daryl and she gave Def a big hug. Then she said: "I'm sorry I called you an uneducated wap the other night. I was just so pissed off. I just have always liked younger guys; they're so easy to dominate. Remember, I'm the one who is educated with my associate's degree in underwater basket weaving. But lest you forget, I am the dominatrix in this marriage."

Then she pulled out an envelope with a picture of Def and Cruisin kissing.

"I got this in the mail today."

Def frowned as he looked at the picture.

"She's not even a white girl. I didn't know you liked dark meat," said Daryl with her hands defiantly on her hips.

"I can explain. It's not what it seems to be. I was just happy and gave her a kiss. That's all," explained Def.

"I don't believe you. I'm getting my switch and you, hubby dear, are getting a well-deserved spanking."

When Def heard that, he ran to the front door but found that he was locked in and Daryl had the only key. By this time, she had her bullwhip and was already lashing him with it. Each time it hit him, the sting brought tears to his eyes. From Daryl's point of view, Def had to be taught a lesson periodically and her bullwhip came in handy. After about twenty minutes, Daryl stopped.

"You only kiss me, not Cruizin. You understand?"

"Yes, honey, I do."

"Now, get up. We have more planning to do."

***

Over the next several weeks Con and Tim went to the Napa County Library. While Tim diverted the librarian's attention with questions of how to find certain books, e-books, and records, Con would take one book after another and slyly put them in his large coat pockets. This time he stole the novel *Plato's Love* and *Seasonings of the Milky Way*, among others. Once he gave Tim the signal, Tim would wander back in the stacks while Con would go out to the car and put his coat filled with several books in the trunk. Minutes later Tim would come out to the car and, once in, would smile with satisfaction that Con had stolen even more of Kent's books.

"Easy pickins," commented Con. "Almost as easy as Calistoga and Yountville."

"Daryl is going to be just delighted when we tell her. Kent is being taught a lesson by the Saint Clements Connection."

"I'm such a proud member," said Con as he reached into a bag of knickknacks on the back seat floor and pulled out a certificate saying he had earned in Boy Scouts the distinction of *Ad Altare Dei* (at the altar of God) which means, among other things, Con is morally straight.

"You earned this?" said Tim.

"Long time ago," mumbled Con. "It meant something at the time. But I've moved on."

"You can say that again," said Tim, scratching some moss off of one of his incisors.

***

The next day when Def came home from work, another bottle of champagne sat in ice on the dining room table.

"More champagne? Are we celebrating something?"

"Just heard from Tim that Con has now stolen all of Kent's books at the Napa County Library."

"All of them?"

"All of them," confirmed Daryl who danced around like she was just asked to the senior prom.

"Boy, Con sure is a great thief! Every last one of them! Wow," he said, pouring the champagne.

***

"What are you doing?" asked Conrad.

"Showing my contempt for that bastard!" affirmed Tim.

"By using pages of his book as toilet paper?"

"You damn right," answered Tim.

"Don't be so foolish. We can sell them and make a profit off our stolen goods. People do it all the time."

"You don't think I should do it?"

"You're losing money by doing that."

"Okay, I'll stop."

"How many pages have you used?"

"Maybe thirty or forty."

"No one's going to want a book with that many pages gone."

This did make sense to Tim. Con had a point.

"Now what about the poison?"

"I can get some at our drug store. The druggist is big supporter of our beer. He'll do anything for me because I have the gift of gab and am always selling our varieties of beer to him and his friends in the beer industry."

"It'll be the end of that bastard for good at our next reunion," said Con.

In the meantime, Tim visited his wife who was bed-ridden in a room sponsored by the churh. His daughter and his grandsons were often there and they loved to see grandpa Tim.

***

After more thefts of Dawson's books, including *The Mysterious Death of Roberta Margate,* by Con, Daryl, who expected complete loyalty from Con and Tim to stay in good standing as original members of the Saint Clements Connection, asked Tim to demand that Con leave his wife Shirley, or, as Con liked to say it, his bride. At first Con refused. His bride could not believe Tim would ask her husband to do such a thing.

"Who does he think he is," she asked in a shocking response.

"Well, he *was* voted 'Most Talented' and was elected 'Student Body Treasurer' in our high school class."

"I don't care if he was voted 'Most Likely To Be a Jackass.' You have done what both Daryl and Tim have asked you to do and we have all of these stolen books in the house. And now they ask you to do that," she said with a resentful tone. "Well, I don't believe in divorce even if they ask you to leave me. And neither does the church."

Con just shrugged his shoulders with a sigh. His loyalty to Tim and Daryl was as strong as Deft's was to Daryl, although Def's loyalty had more of a tone of obedience based on fear.

The next day, Shirley called her priest, one Father Louis, and asked if she could see him as soon as possible. She drove to Saint Anne's Catholic Church and went into the chapel where Father Louis was going over his notes for his sermon at this week's mass. This week was the feastday for Saint Clement.

"Shirley, it's always a delight to see you. I hope all is well for you and Con and the family."

"That's what I called about. We have a serious situation in our house."

A look of concern mapped Father Louis' face.

"We can talk more privately in my study," he said.

Once inside, Shirley took a seat.

76

"Would you like some water? Or coffee?"

"Water would be fine. Thank you," said Shirley. He gave her a glass of water and sat down so they could talk face to face.

"This week's mass is also the feastday for Saint Clement."

"Interestingly, Con's friend Tim had a father named Clement."

"Good Catholic name, especially since Clement was a pope long ago," commented Louis, gently stroking his silver and black mustache.

"So what is the situation?"

"Con's friend Tim has demanded that Con leave me."

"Con leave you. Why?"

"It's a loyalty thing."

"A loyalty thing?"

"Yes. They've been friends for so long since they went to Saint Clements School for the first eight grades. So did their other friend, Daryl Shrouden, who is the ringleader of the Saint Clements Connection."

"What does she have to do with it?" "She decided to attack or harm in any way she could the author Kent Dawson because he told her he would escort her anytime and anywhere, especially since he had been her Halloween queen escort in the twelfth grade."

"Why would that upset her? It sounds flattering."

"She obviously took it the wrong way and interpreted it as though he was making fun of her and even coming on to her. So when she returned to her home in Maryland, she told her husband who thought he should do something about it."

For a minute, Father Louis thoughtfully stroked his mustache, then said:

"You think he would come in to talk about it?"

"It is hard to say. I think he will be upset that I came to our priest to talk about it."

"I could call him and invite him to lunch."

"Would you? It would mean so much to me."

"I'll do it and pray for you both," said Louis.

***

"You did what?"

"I went to talk to our priest. I don't believe in divorce, Con. Just because Tim asks you to leave me, doesn't mean you have to do it."

"But he expects my loyalty and so does Daryl."

Just then the phone rang.

"It's Father Louis." Con gave Shirley a mean and nasty look as he grudgingly took the phone.

"Hello Father Louis. How are you? You what?"

"Yeah, we could do that. Okay. Tomorrow at ten. See you then."

"Seems our priest wants to have brunch at Bruno's. I'll talk to him but I'm not changing my mind. You were foolish to drag him into this situation. You know how loyal I am to Tim. After all, he was voted 'Most Talented' in our high school class."

"I don't care if he was voted dog catcher. He should not have that kind of influence over you! Especially when it comes to you and I. It's our marriage we're talking about! What happened to 'till death do us part?'"

"Things have changed. I'm loyal to Tim and Daryl and so is Daryl's hubby, Def."

***

"Father Louis. I apologize for Shirley dragging you into this," he said as he drank some coffee.

"I'm your priest for you and your family. She's concerned about this friend who says you have to leave her. Are you so loyal to this friend that he can demand such a thing?"

"We've been friends for so long since we were at Saint Clements together for eight years."

"But I don't understand why he can destroy your marriage and family with such a demand?"

"I didn't think you would understand."

"And you've been stealing books by Kent Dawson from the Napa County Library? We're talking about stealing in addition to divorce?"

"I thought I knew you. We've always had cordial relations but now —"

Con simply shrugged his shoulders as though he was helpless to do anything about it.

"I always thought you had some balls but you apparently don't have the balls to stand up to this guy Tim and..."

"We all have our limitations," said Con, getting up from their table and, making an about face, promptly left. Father Louis paid for their coffees.

***

At their next high school reunion, they noticed Kent wore his blue block sweater with a gold N for photos of him and his wife. Although Con had won a letter in tennis for Napa High, Tim was simply not a good enough athlete to make the cut in any sport he tried out for. When Kent appeared in his block sweater, this only made Tim even more jealous and envious since it pointed out his limitations compared to Kent. This reminded him of the jealousy he felt when Kent was the leading scorer with one hundred fifty-four points for the season when they played on the same team coached by that legendary city league coach, Texas John Stoddart.

In the meantime, Daryl sat at her table gossiping with other women such as Marlena Pantolini and Zofia Mandrake who also disliked Kent but did not hate him with the degree of viciousness Daryl had for him. To trash talk someone she did not like was her technique to galvanize dislike for that person. Marlena and Zofia were like Daryl preaching to the choir; they already disliked Kent for whatever reason.

But everyone was having a great time with old friends. Tim had got some poison which was colorless and odorless and the plan was for Con to put it in one of Kent's drinks. And that would be the end of Kent. As the evening wore on, more and more people were high if not drunk. Nobody seemed to notice when Kent got his third highball and, drinking it, soon collapsed on the floor. At that moment, both Tim and Con slipped out the door and drove off in different cars. Tim headed for his home in Antioch and Con headed for his home in Petaluma. Their plan seemed to go off without a hitch. Daryl and others came over to where Kent lay sprawled on the floor. She put on a good act about how much she admired Kent and that he was one of her favorite authors. She went on and on about how honored she was to know him and be her classmate. Meanwhile, ambulance technicians had to wade through the crowd and police had arrived. The doors were locked so no one could leave. Everyone was asked to give a DNA sample to determine if anyone there could have done this. But Con and Tim were long gone.

Detectives working with the police department began working on the case. Forensic science was able to determine that the kind of poison found at Kent's autopsy was a kind sold only in Antioch. Detectives in Antioch interrogated the druggist who sold the poison and that he was a friend of beer salesman Tim. But Tim had gone to Petaluma to hide out at Con's place and so far Tim had not been found.

"I didn't get into this to be part of a murder," began Con.

"But you want to remain in good standing of the Saint Clements Connection, don't you?" asked Tim. "And Daryl loved the plan from the very beginning when we first approached her with it."

Con nodded with a sigh. He felt like he was in quicksand; the more he wriggled and wondered about it, the more he sank deeper.

***

Daryl attended Kent's funeral and found it hard to maintain a straight face as his wife and kids sobbed and cried. She felt like throwing up as other classmates praised Kent to the skies and offered sympathy and consolation to his family and close friends. She felt no remorse or shame at Kent's murder. To her, it was good to have him out of the way.

She had one more plan to undermine Kent even in death. After a number of days, his coffin was lowered into the Eternal Rest cemetery ground with a headstone that read: Kent B. Dawson 1948-2018. She thought it would be great to have a piece of his headstone for her mantelpiece back home so both she and Def could be reminded how they had destroyed a classmate and author who had offended her dignity.

On an evening that was both moonless and starless, Daryl drove up with Con and Tim to the cemetery gate. The plan was for Daryl to drive while Con and Tim went over the gate with a sledge hammer and other tools to get part of the headstone for Daryl to take back to Maryland. Tim also took along a large chisel to remove Kent's name and dates so that it would seem Kent had never existed. That is how deep his jealousy and envy were as long as he could remember.

He would finally feel good once Kent was obliterated completely.

It was not long before the sledge hammer blows were heard by not only a night owl cemetery caretaker but neighbors who lived across the street. Lights in their homes began turning on. Tim had also entirely removed Dawson's name and dates. Suddenly a police squad car pulled up behind Daryl's car. As the officer was coming up to her window, Daryl pulled out and sped down the street. The officer with sirens going was in hot pursuit.

"Hey, Daryl just left us here," said Con in a low voice.

"Let's get out of here," murmured Tim who headed for the gate until another squad car pulled up with its lights flashing. Both Tim and Con began running up the hill and avenues of the cemetery. Cops with Beretta M9 semi-automatic pistols drawn and bright flashlights ran after them. Both Tim and Con hid behind family tombs. But the cops were relentless. Now more squad cars were at the cemetery gate with silent lights flashing. After awhile both Tim and Con could run no more, not at their age.

One officer, Mike Roth barked: "Lie face down on the ground with your hands behind your heads. Now cuff 'em," They were taken by squad car to the police station where they were booked, finger printed, and put in jail. Meanwhile the area around Kent's grave was cordoned off as a crime scene. After a long chase past Hagen Road and Big Ranch Road, Daryl was finally cornered and caught. She, too, went to jail.

She spit in Officer Roth's face and screamed that she was the ringleader of the Saint Clements Connection.

To which Roth replied: "I don't care if you're the ringleader of Assholes Anonymous. You're going to be off the streets for a long time, you sleeze-ball."

Though they had the best lawyers money can buy, all three were convicted for resisting arrest, stealing from private property, attacking a police officer, not to mention conspiracy to commit premeditated murder. Even Def was arrested and put in jail. All four ended up with a sentence of life in prison with no possibility of parole. And all four died in prison.

Epilogue

D espite their efforts, and after many years, Dawson's play, *Pele's Lover*, is required reading in literature and humanities classes to graduate from high school on the islands of Maui, Oahu, Kailua, and the big island Hawai'i. Even some libraries that held his books during his lifetime, kept some of his books while others took them off the shelves and sold them as used books to raise funds for the library. Ironically, as news got out of all the efforts to steal Kent's books, many avid readers felt they must be good for people to try to steal them. So sales of his books increased until they were bestsellers in various places, including America.

Indian Summer's Dream

Thoughts of the finality of his father's death haunted him. He could not manage to cease dwelling upon a loss that was forever. Long August days stretched like arms in an El Greco painting into Indian summer. At night such thoughts so disturbed him that once he even was afraid to go to sleep for fear he would never wake again, that he, too, would be gone. Forever.

It had been weeks since he had seen his father's face. How different Papa looked. How he lay there in the casket. How friends and family solemnly approach it, paused, whispered, and each had imprinted on the retina of the eye their last picture of him. Papa had been dressed in a bluish tweed suit, his dark hands folded on his chest, his wedding band on his finger, all strictly convention. He appeared so different.

At this juncture, where hellos and goodbyes are dawns apart, he was amazed how friends sprung out of the network of their common humanity. People really were kind. It was as though his father's face was their mirror too. Pallbearer Bill Templeton said: "I've lost a part of me." Long-time friend Jim Bosche whispered: "He was the best. We're gonna miss him." There was also so much food. Chicken both grilled and fried, mashed and scalloped potatoes, spinach, steak, garden salads, deviled eggs, sodas, sliced carrots and tomatoes, freshly-perked coffee, and green tea. It was as if when folks died the survivors had to have food lest they grow hungry.

His mother never recovered. Not after thirty-eight years of marriage. It was so hard for her. Everything changed. Her entire world.

He had once dreamed of his parents' deaths. He had awakened with a start. But he realized it was only a dream.

Now he was twenty-eight. Dream had turned into reality. The loss was an abyss, an ever-widening abyss when care was that close was in the game. It was hard to take. Diamond-hard.

His brother, Lamar, did not say much. Maybe he did not know what to say when it came to such transitions. It was better not to even think about such things. You had to love, to continue, he thought.

Martha, his sister, had cared for Papa during the long and agonizing months of his illness. She thus felt the profound sense of loss as well as a deep sense of relief from the rounds of care. She would soon be able to turn her attention back to her husband and daughters.

At their last meeting he and Papa had been strangers. Papa had been understandably irritable. The cancer had spread, first through the inner lining of the left. Long Surgery could have stopped the spread had Papa not already had pneumonia in his right lung. Although the pneumonia eventually cleared, Papa grew more and more isolated. He was so weak, due to weight loss and lack of appetite, the surgery was thought to be no longer an option. Dr. Miksa and his staff had not recommended surgery because it would have made Papa's condition more dangerous. It was just a matter of months even weeks; each day became a death rehearsal. At Papa's request, Dr. Miksa did not hint of the extent of the severity of Papa's illness. The family was thus kept in ignorance. Throughout the long days of early summer Papa could hear the periodic dull thuds of apricots that had ripened and fallen on the ground outside his bedroom window. Zucchini as well ripened in the lazy summer's sun.

His mother did not realize how sick Papa really was. Papa was secretive and stoical about the severity of his condition. Yet his mother felt the distance, the ever-parting waves on the seas that separated them. Finally, in mid-July, he remembered, she had to get away from the pain and the parting. She flew to Tennessee to visit relatives, including a son who was a student in summer school at Vanderbilt.

Even two thousand miles away could not get Papa off his mother's thoughts. She enjoyed the dancing would-be stars at Opryland; the musicians hoping to cut a record and make it big at the various record companies on Music Row and Studio B where Elvis Presley recorded many of his songs; the fascinating history of the Hermitage, the home of President Andrew Jackson; and the serenity and art of the Cheekwood Botanical Gardens. Even the white pillars of Nashville's Belle Meade Mansion and the statue of Athena, Greek goddess of wisdom, at the Parthenon, a replica of the Parthenon that stood on the Acropolis in ancient Athens, Greece, momentarily captured her attention. At night, however, her thoughts raced from Tennessee to California. Phone calls yielded from Martha a mixture of apprehension and thinly-disguised assurances.

After two weeks, she just had to fly home. She bought Davy Crockett coonskin caps and toys for Martha's girls, said goodbye to her relatives and son, and turned her thoughts homeward bound as Nashville lights disappeared in jet windows. Something told her it was time to resume with Martha the care of Papa. Family support in times of crisis was what made such junctures bearable at all.

When his mother arrived home, joy seemed everywhere, even in Papa's distant face. He even managed a smile at the coonskin caps. He never looked so good. It was as though everything would be better, that tomorrow would bring a sunnier day. A glow, translucent, curiously enough, bathed his face. Even the seventy-three pounds he had lost from chemotherapy in the last six months did not seem to intrude upon the touch of arms who had shared thirty-eight years. Little did his mother suspect.

He remembered how the news came. It was like hang gliding over a ridge of oak-clustered hills, hay-colored in late-July bloom. The call from his sister. Shocked. Broken. Martha, a courage in bones, discovered the blood-streaked sheets. His death had come in the night. It was not like Byron's gallant efforts on behalf of Greek independence; nor was it a death by dismemberment by a serial killer; or death among many other faceless numbers on battlefields such as Gettysburg, Verdun, Pearl Harbor, the Somme, Gallipoli, Wounded Knee Creek, Sluys, or The Bulge. It was not that conventional. His death was quiet and at home, not hospital centered. His death simply came: the metastasizing cancer cells had severed blood vessels in the lung and hemorrhaging resulted. Small blood puddles lay near the bed where he had tried to cough away the air-drowning blood.

Even as Martha called an ambulance, the mid-morning heat quivered from the asphalt of Foster Road and the already reddish color on the Santa Rosa plums his father had grafted in the spring deepened. The ambulance siren seemed somehow muted. The head on this last July day seemed to muffle drums of passing blood and bone. All other concerns now seemed trivial, even petty. Even nightly denials by the President concerning alleged knowledge of the Watergate break-in slipped into irrelevance. Death trivializes our petty graspings, he thought.

Martha was strong. Her grief was not brief; it would extend for years. She alone would visit his grave on a regular basis while the rest of the family tried to somehow forget in order to live. The guilt, the resentment, the entire process first had to be cut short due to business considerations. From casket and cemetery selection down to the color of Papa's last suit were considerations that had to be faced. Such were the concerns for a family that faced a death in the family for the first time. His mother was in no shape to make such decisions; her eyes were bloodshot. Martha and her Vanderbilt son who had flown home from Nashville were the ones who made such choices; Lamar, forty miles away, was keeping his mind off the scene from throwing himself ever more fitfully into his family and his work.

Soon the initial shock began to wear off; reality insinuated itself. Never again the laughter, the jokes. So many things he had wished to say to Papa; if only he had said them. Never would they be said. Right now he wanted to talk to him. As weeks passed, however, the earth turned a deeper hay color; the Santa Rosa plums ripened into juicier maroon morsels. Zuchini were picked when tender; the apricots were gathered in time. Amid Indian summer days a hint of autumn was yet in the air. Rivers continued to flow from mountains to the sea.

There was nothing else, he thought. You died and that was it. Yet death was horrible, so personal, so devastating when it touched your life and those for whom you deeply cared. Finality was what hurt. He always tried to view things scientifically. The women at the funeral were sentimental. His mother relied on faith; Martha's strength sprang from not only her faith but her sheer determination to survive. He remembered sitting quietly, almost lost in his own thought, as Reverend Wolter Vanbrugge painted a word picture of a ship receding over the horizon. Death, he said, was a farewell and a time to look life's mysteries in the eyes.

The church organist, Kara Melton, played "Abide With Me" in a dirgeful manner; he remembered comforting his mother and staring at a wreath of red roses next to the open casket. Once the eulogy and the music and the hymns were over, guests filed by the casket to take one last look. That face he would not forget: Papa's face was like clay that had been smoothed. He remembered how sex had become almost an obsession; life could grasp at straws that way. Sex and death were kissing cousins; an affirmation of life no matter what. He had nudged next to the tenuous edges of human finitude.

One evening several weeks later, he was reclining on the screened porchway of the house. A lamp was on but not directly overhead. The rattan chaise lounge was comfortable even though he lay on his right side away from the lamp. The lamp was the only genesis of light. Familiar sounds of crickets and the low, nearly inaudible hum of the television inside the house could be heard. Slowly he slid into a light sleep; in fact he was quite aware of everything at once. He looked over his shoulder. Gradually it dawned on him the leg he saw out of the corner of his eye was the same leg sticking out from under Papa's bed sheet he had seen numerous times during

Papa's last days. He did not turn to gaze at the rest of his body. He knew it was Papa; it had to be.

"We're at a loss," he began.

"You needn't be," the voice replied in almost inaudible tones.

"You mean everything is okay?"

"Yes. Very well," came the reply.

"But it's horrible. Mom is taking it the worst," he said in half-awe.

"Everything's all right," came the reply.

"How can you say that?"

"It just is. Just is. No need to worry," came the reply. He peered over his shoulder. The legs were still there, reclining. There was a long silence; the crickets now seemed far in the distance, the light more dim. Then he continued:

"But all the times we could've said. The finality of it."

"There's no need to worry. Believe me. All is well."

At that moment he awoke. He did not say anything to anyone. He was reassured. A wake of calm fan-tailed over him like a warm, turquoise sea. Clutches of finality no longer gripped him. Serenity now massaged his fear, his loss, and his anxiety. A dream, he thought, only a dream. He could have seen a ghost or possibly a reincarnation of his father, but he did not. He only saw his legs. Perhaps waking was only a dream among other dreams. From that night forward, he felt that there was something that did not die, a shadow that somehow remained. He did not know why or even how.

For the first time in weeks he finally slept soundly and deeply. He never slept so well as he did after this dream.

The Night the Bulldozers Came

"I'm waiting for a bulldozer to crash through my office sometime and clear my desk of papers," Doc Hinto once said. His office was a cubbyhole decorated with modern designs, family portraits, and a desk and telephone. It was off the Stanford campus or you thought so by the time you had passed the radiation lab, the engineering buildings, and the parking lot that resembled a football field.

I don't know what got into me when I awoke at half past twelve one night in late February. I looked around, blinked, and sprang out of bed. Putting on my coat, I dashed down the corridor and out into the crisp, clear night. I had heard the sounds of bulldozers weaving about in my head, like the rattling of thousands of miniature bells, softly clanging until my mind felt as if it would expand out to the edge of the universe and suddenly stop when time reached zero.

Dashing across the Spanish style quadrangle, I saw the face of Christ on the church bathed in iridescent light as purple as the evening. I felt timeless, out of and beyond time. I was nowhere and everywhere at once. What about the Floridian who worked so late? Wasn't he everywhere at once? Doc Hinto was from the "buckle on the Bible belt," Gainesville, Florida. He didn't like it there and I suspect he didn't like it here either.

I crossed Panama Drive, jogged through the half-muddy sidewalks, under the hanging moss that covered the parking lot like a shaggy blanket. Rounding the bend, I saw a light from his office. I ran to the green door, banging my fists on it, kicking it. Then footsteps. He opened the door, his red, pudgy chin-clefted face seeming weary from his writing for New York publishers.

"What's wrong, Mr. B?" he asked in his soft accent.

"What's wrong?" I exclaimed. "The bulldozers are coming that's what's wrong."

"I've heard of Santa Claus coming. But I never…"

"What did you have tonight? Bourbon? Southern Comfort? Hot Toddy? Whiskey Sour? A Dry Martini?" he said, his tone unchanged.

"No, no, no. I'm not drunk, Doc. Honest."

"Come in and take a load off your feet," he said quietly trying to get back to his work. A sheet of paper was tucked in his typewriter as we entered the cubbyhole.

"Now, Mr. B., you know as well as I no bulldozers are coming this way. Besides, even if they were coming, I'd simply go out and salute them. So calm yourself. Would you like some coffee to sober up?"

"I told you. I told you I am not drunk. I tell you I heard the bulldozers coming straight for your office. I honestly did. Now you must know how Georgians felt when they heard General Sherman was cutting through Georgia to the sea."

"How can I feel that way when I'm not a southern sympathizer? What are you trying to do, enter my subscription to Atlanta magazine? Or trying to get my mother's recipe for good old fashioned Kentucky Mint Juleps? Aha, Mr. B., I think I've got your little game. You mean to tell me you came running all the way over here to make me feel like a Georgian so I'd give you some of the pecan pie my mother sent me in today's mail? Come, come, Mr. B. I just don't believe Georgians felt that way nor do I welcome your trying to gain access to my Pecan Pie or, to say the least, to my Mint Julep recipe while I editorialize in the *Washington Reporter*."

He laughed it off and began staring at the window. Before I knew it, his mouth dropped open as he stared out into the night. A light, pink snow had fallen on the lawn outside and lined up on all sides were bulldozers with their blades aimed right at old Doc. He could not believe it. He turned to me, his face now pale with shock.

"My God, bulldozers *are* out there. At least four or five of them." He looked back at me, his mouth opened wider.

"Each driver, if I'm not mistaken, is one of the students I gave low grades to last quarter. Good God, am I dreaming? Mr. B. do I look all right to you?"

"You do look a little pale, Doc. Didn't I tell you there were bulldozers out there?"

"Yes, but I didn't believe..." He stared out the window again, shaking his head slightly. "Good grief! They're starting their motors. I'd better evacuate. Let me see. Anything I need?" He picked up a stack of the *New Republic* and began to go out the door. He leaned back in.

"Mr. B?"

"Yes, Doc."

"If you can get rid of them, I'll, I'll give you that recipe."

"I don't need your recipe, Doc. I tell you what, why don't you just move your desk out the door and let them shove all these papers off?"

"I don't think they want the desk. They want me, Mr. B. Me." He took off and I followed.

"*Now*, do you know what the Georgians felt like?"

"Yes. I must admit I do. Damn that Sherman anyway. Why does he have to come back and haunt me. I studied him in college, you know."

We passed through the door and out onto the new-fallen snow where the bulldozers were readied. Presently, Doc pulled out his hanky as a symbol of truce.

"One thing about it, Mr. B."

"What's that, Doc?"

"We southerners never seem to finish surrendering, do we?"

"I guess not, Doc." At that moment, he threw up his hands and surrendered.

Hey, Short Stuff!

A theme of Jean-Paul Sartre's play *No Exit* is "hell is other people." Often this is true. I went to a camera shop not long ago and was standing next to the glass counter trying to figure out how much I should put down for a radio on layaway. While I pondered where my money should go, this round-faced guy was giving me the once over. It was embarrassing being stared at. People can be so nosy; they always want to know what you're thinking about and what you're going to do next. Well, this pudgy guy kept staring at me. Beads of sweat appeared on my forehead and everything suddenly became too hot. The clerk, a Mrs. Lazzlo, said:

"How much would you like to put down?"

I didn't really know. She was getting rather impatient for my reply and said:

"Ten dollars?"

Still I made no motion one way or the other.

"Six dollars?"

To this I nodded agreement. All the while this guy kept his eyes glued on me as if I were the President or something. I paid the money and left the store. Needless to say, I was relieved to get out of there and into my car. It was nice and cool out. A slight rain had begun. I turned on the windshield wipers and headed off into the glare of headlights on my way home.

Rain is really inspiring; at least it is to me. It seems like heaven is crying out and trying to wash away the evil doings on the earth. Rain is our catharsis; we have to alter our living to adjust. And thunder is as if thousands of drums were announcing heaven's dissatisfaction. I guess people don't really give a hoot when they're more concerned with own security. Everyone, it seems, is out for their personal gain. People can be so impersonal at times, not caring who legs they trample on. I like those people who are not nosy, but are friendly without any personal motivations. But some people will taunt you and make your life miserable when they can.

When I was at a meeting recently there were two jackasses in the front row. One was rather short in height with close-clipped wavy black hair and wore dark-framed glasses. The other was much taller with dark brown hair and possessed a grin so nauseating I could not stand to look at it. His name was Broc and the former was called Jarvis.

During the coffee break, which is somehow always injected into a meeting to make it last longer, these two were standing around telling ribald jokes and a having a jackass time of it. The jokes were stale, but intellectual level was such that they suited them fine and dandy. Unfortunately, I knew them and they were accustomed to making snide observations whether the occasion warranted it or not. Broc approached and said:

"How goes it, shorty?" That's what he always called me.

"All right," I replied unenthusiastically.

"Whatcha been doin' lately? Haven't seen you around," he began.

"Nothing much," came my reply. Boy, that punk could really get on my nerves.

"How's your love life, shorty? Find anyone short enough for ya?" he said with a jeering tone.

"Why don't you shut up, huh?"

"Now, shorty..." He waved to Jarvis who was eager for more entertainment. Those jackasses, I thought. I began moving toward the door, but Jarvis wanted to join Brok in the idle tomfoolery. Those asses. Ye gods they make me sick!

"Hey, gang, It's good ole, shorty..."

He strode over with the air of self-anointed god and the strut of a Rhode Island red rooster. The others began heading toward me. I was in for it now. I pretended it did not bother me for that is what I must do to ward off further offensive thrusts. I could not help it if I am short. That's the way it is, though. Very short guys and very tall ones always have the middle group jealous. Sweat beads were really beginning to form, those jackasses, always picking on innocent bystanders.

"How's the short stuff, today?" smirked Broc with a s disgusting air of superiority. You would think he was a graduate of some prestigious school or academy. He really got on my nerves. It was beginning to get stuffy. Broc put his paw on my shoulder and I brusquely pushed it off. His eyes peered into the depths of mine. I was angry and ready for his head on a stake. Repressed anger is hellish.

"Whatsa matter, shorty?" He said it so sarcastically it was sickening. With that he put his hand on my head and petted it like a dog. I began swinging but he held me at arm's length much to the overwhelming approval of the crowd. My face was red hot.

"Just get your damn hands off me, you jackass," I yelled. Broc looked surprised and backed away while mocking my ferocious behavior. What torture! I hated him.

I wheeled around, yanked open the door and ran in a wild frenzy down to the end of the hallway. The others followed me out the door and amid bursts of joyous laughter ridiculed me. I pushed open the swinging doors and the cold, rainy wet day was ever evident as I staggered out the door, down the brick steps and began to run, but stumbled on a marshland of saturated grass. My legs were soaked to the skin. I ran to the over-hanging wing of a nearby lumber dealer. The smells of freshly-cut timber were everywhere. Sawdust in its powderly aroma reached my nostrils and filled them as full as lungs could hold. The wood was probably from Oregon; that's where most of our wood comes from anyway. A tall stack of lumber created a dry place where I could sit. I sat down, my pants sopped with rainwater and tears ran down my cheeks. I kept uttering to myself:

"Man's inhumanity to man"
"Man's inhumanity to man"

I hated the world then. After my mind cleared, I remembered where the car was and got in and drove home. It was really raining out now and splotches of rain kept the wipers going vigorously. The next day, the sun came out and off to the eastern horizon, a rainbow appeared in most eye-fetching yellows, greens, purples, oranges, and blues. I loved the world. There was a lake not far from my home. I walked up there and lay down in the grass on a blanket. Nature was paradise untouched where man had not yet taken it over; wilderness was a soothing balm for the soul. There I could relax with a faint breeze breathing across the shimmering waters and small firs abounding while a doe and two fauns cautiously sniffed a scent, then went down to the water's edge for a drink. What bliss and peace. I knew in my heart this was the good side of the world, especially when like-minded people were also included.

The Hunt

When blackbirds began to eat the cherries on the cherry tree and the peaches on the peach tree or those that had already fallen to the ground, it was obvious no one would buy such a damaged crop. So that morning his father had instructed him to kill all the blackbirds that he could find with a pellet gun he had bought from the Caymus gun shop in town.

The birds had swooped down upon the long gold cat enough; his father had said to protect their nest up in the evergreen tree. And besides, the gold cat was more than hungry, its stomach lean from little food in the past few weeks.

So he loaded the rifle carefully and set out along the tall eucalyptus trees that bordered the dirt road next to their place, their branches swaying with the wind that filtered through the leaves.

The shrill screech of the blackbirds kept them clear in his head from the sparrows and jays and robins that fed in the same place. He saw one perched upon a bare branch that swayed; he aimed, fired and saw it sit there still. He cocked the rifle. Again he fired. This time it swooped limp to the ground, its wings vibrating and hurt.

The gold cat bounded over to it, clamping it between its sharp pointed teeth and running off. He cocked it again and squinted into the leaning eucalyptus leaves that seemed to be hanging fingers of shining ice in the sun's reflection. He saw one that had caught on to the game and quickly flew lazily over him. He shot and missed. The bird flew back among the waving branches and he shot into them, still missing at each firing. He then hid under a canopy that offered him not only shade but camouflage. He waiting intently, listening to each shrill cry of the bird that had just eluded him.

He heard the cry and he crept out slowly, keeping as close as he could to the shrubs surrounding the canopy. The black profile of the bird sat squarely facing him and he raised the gun to his shoulder. He shot and missed again.

Again the bird flew over him as if to make his lost shots as the bird knew he could not hit him in flight. He was not that experienced of a hunter. By this time, the cat, its stomach obviously full, emerged from a nearby bush, licking its muzzle as if awaiting another meal, licking its paws and washing its face.

He wanted this bird more with each passing moment, but it flew over him again and again. The cat would love this one for dinner, he thought. But every time he shot, he missed and the bullets flew off into space. The bird knew. He knew. He got six others that day but not the one he wanted.

That evening, after it became too dark to see, he heard the one, the one he wanted, screeching proudly into the sky. He turned on his lamp and read *Field and Stream* until midnight, then turned out the light and rolled over and slept soundly. The morning flooded its light into the venetian blinds of his window. He got up, had bacon, pancakes and eggs for breakfast, and began the morning hunt, peering high into the tree tops. It saw him and screeched twice then flew out over him, repeating what he had done the day before.

He could hear his father drive up the long gravel driveway to the house. He was home early. The rifle shot cracked out, echoing long and almost silent, waving across the sky and echoing against the tree trunks. The proud bird flew across the clouds as backdrop, pausing and swooping, then flapping its wings furiously, soaring like an eagle, lighting into the top branches of a squatty green oak.

He crept up slowly, ever slowly and pointed the barrel through a break in the shrub. The rifle shot cracked the air as he squeezed the trigger; the bird got away, streaking across the pink horizon like an arrow, its streamlined body aiming for the protective eucalyptus branches.

The door closed just loud enough for him to hear; the gold cat rested on its haunches in the bushes, the long dangling leaves tickling its ear, lazily. His father approached with a grey coat with buttoned sleeves, his thin light mustache closely cut.

"How many today?" he asked the boy.

"Four."

"Four?" he exclaimed. The boy turned around.

"Why, yes. I know it's not as many as yesterday but..."

"That's all right, son. The day isn't over yet," he said gazing up at the sun. Then he continued. "You ever get the one you wanted?" The boy shook his head, seeming disappointed in himself.

"Keep shootin' you're bound to get him. If you don't you'll hit one of those stars," he said chuckling.

"The stars don't come out in the day, do they?"

"Probably. But you can only see 'em at night," he said, trudging up the hill to feed the chickens. The boy returned to the shrubbery and in the twinkling of an eye, one of the birds landed on a long telephone wire, sitting there with its wing spread. He aimed and fired. The blackbird fell to the ground, its wings crushed and minute pink blobs of blood like still eyes appeared on the wing. The gold cat dashed to the scene, pawing it and playing with the injured bird.

This time, however, the cat did not wish to eat the bird; he only played with it. The boy could not understand; the cat had always eaten the birds he'd killed before. Why was this one different?

Almost like a reading of the minds, his father came down the hill and paused behind him.

"What's wrong?" he asked his son.

"The cat, he won't eat that bird I just shot for him."

"Well, you know he's probably full. Cats are like people, they can only eat so much. Besides, he may prefer filet mignon at this point," he said eyeing the boy, standing with his gun pointed down.

"I guesso," said the boy demurely. "He's already had four; I guess I can't expect him to eat too many, huh?" His father shook his head and said no. The night fell as quickly as the morning had risen.

The next day was spent doing the chores and shooting intermittently at the blackbirds. He got nine but not the one that continually hovered over him, each and every day until monotony set in and he almost went crazy so strong was his desire to kill the bird. Soon he had, with his faithful rifle, killed over forty birds until there was only the one left, the proud one. The boy became ever so blood thirsty; he wanted that last one, the most prized one, so badly.

Its shrill call sent him flying out the kitchen door to load his rifle and see where the bird was in the tree. He saw it, aimed, and tried to pull the trigger but could not; he was breathing too hard and the sight kept wavering back and forth without aiming straight for the blackbird. Meanwhile the bird perched on a bare set of limbs that thrust out into the dying sun, tossing gently with the wind, making the shrill call to him. He steadied the rifle again, pressing it to his shoulder, confident he would get it this time. No. The sight kept wavering, but again he shot and missed. Enraged, his face turning scarlet from his failures, he ran after the bird firing wildly into the eucalyptus branches, screaming and swearing at the top of his lungs. The bird calmly flew over him, floating on the air then flapping wildly its wings and soaring back into the oak for a moment's perch.

The door slammed and his father emerged, walking toward him, moving in a fast pace.

"What's wrong now?" he said.

"Oh, oh," was all the boy could say.

"Couldn't get him?" The boy shook his head.

"You can't get all of 'em, even though you think you can, son. Come on in and sit down."

The boy walked into a large garage-like room with stuffed pheasants, owls, and deer heads, their eyes peering out in silence as an example of the suffering animals endure unfelt by their sporting human predators. They sat down on the sofas that faced one another. Through the large window, they could see the slanted hills, the green valleys, the hanging trees with the sunlight dancing among the leaves as if in ballet, the marshy meadows with butterflies flitting across them, their wings batting the air.

"I've got every last one of them except that one," the boy began, laying his rifle on the side panel made of knotty pine. His father said nothing for the moment but took down a slender book with the name of Hugo on it in red letters.

"So that's the one you want, huh? The one you been after all this time," he said to the boy as he opened the book, licking his fingers to flip the pages.

"Yes, he's the last one. The last one and then there'll be no more blackbirds to eat the cherries and peaches. His father faintly smiled, still turning the pages. He stopped and scanned the page and read to the boy: "'The teeth can look, just as the eye can bite,'" he said, peering over his glasses at his son. The boy made no response. He just sat there wondering all the while.

"You can't get this one, huh?"

"Not yet." Then after a pause:

"You think you'll get him?"

"Maybe. Maybe if I try hard enough," he said, half-assured.

"Maybe," agreed his father. "Member the other day when I said you may just hit one of those stars?" The boy nodded.

"Well, there a time you can hit 'em and a time when you can't. Just depends on when you shoot and how you go about it. There's a time for this bird and all the birds that follow. You see, son, you may not hit this one; and you think there's won't be anymore? No, no, no. There'll be more. Tomorrow."

The boy nodded vaguely, his eyes going up to the owl overhead and back down to his father.

"I guesso," he said, agreeing with him. The boy understood, but he never could kill the proud bird. Every day it flew over him, its wings ceasing in mid-flight as if to taunt him and always soaring back into the eucalyptus branches. The bird's call came to his ears but nothing could be done and secretly he was glad.

The Hook

"Don't drink all that stuff. It's an import," warned James as he took his fishing gear and headed over the gentle hill to the leeward side of Lake Berryessa. "I'll probably come get some more." The label on the bottle read Old Adam's Ale.

"You don't think I'd drink all *that*, do you?" I replied. He grinned but made no reply as he disappeared. Our boat was tied to a low-hanging limb.

As morning broke, lupines carpeted the northern flank of hills. Clouds wispy here and there mapped the sky. Clusters of mustard waved bright yellow in the breezes of spring. Fishing was slow; I wondered how James was faring as I took another swallow. After awhile, I began to feel light-headed. If you don't get a bite, take another swallow of that stuff, I thought. And so I did. Fishing was deep since spring warmth had sent the trout and bass deeper, sometimes into the shadows. Morning drowsily eased into afternoon.

I baited my hook again and cast in. Looking up, I saw a man in a kayak wearing a funny hat on his head. It turned out to be an admiral's hat with a long red plume flowing from it. The kayak turned in my direction. As it drew near our boat, the man barked:

"Have you seen my fleet?"

"Your what?" I said.

"My fleet," he said. He noticed I was staring at his hat and he offered: "Oh, this," he pointed to his hat, "I am an admiral."

"An admiral?"

"Yes. And I have lost my fleet," he added as though this was of utmost importance.

"You've lost your fleet?"

"Yes. Have you seen it? Schooners, two-masted clipper ships."

"No. I haven't seen any fleet around here. This is only a lake, a mirage. No fleet could fit here."

He was now close enough so I could see his thick sideburns, muttonchops, and dark mustache; they were not quite as prominent as his plume that fluttered in the breeze. After a long, almost meditative pause, he said "'Tis no mirage, sir. I must be off to find my fleet". I nodded in agreement. It sounded like a splendid idea.

"Yes, you must be off...Good luck," I said. Off came his admiral's hat. In a courtly gesture, he bowed until his lips almost touched the kayak. Soon he rounded a point of rock just off shore and disappeared. I baited my hook again and cast in. Not long afterwards, I noticed another boat round the bend in the cove. In it a gorilla leisurely rowed, each oar glistening in the sun. He saw my boat and began rowing toward mine.

I looked at what I'd been drinking with its wordless brown paper cover then returned my eyes toward this boat in which sat someone dressed as one of the higher primates.

Our eyes met. He tried to make gestures, such as scratching, to make it seem he was really an ape. Why would anyone dress up as one of the higher primates on a warm spring day and row around this particular portion of the lake? I made up my mind not to say anything.

With barely a sound, his boat nudged mine. Not once did this person's eyes veer from mine. We were in a staring contest. I swallowed hard; I did not know what was going to happen or what would be said. Scratching himself, he continued to stare at me then finally extended his hand and began to pat me down as though looking for a concealed weapon. Was this a stop and frisk situation? There was no probable cause! Why, I was both a fisherman and a taxpayer! This disgusting beast was apparently going to carry this charade as far as he could. That I was becoming upset was obvious. Yet mingled with my disgust was a faint curiosity.

"Get your paws off me," I demanded.

104

His eyes darted to mine and riveted on them as it stopped pawing me. For the first time, I noticed letters on the mud-caked bow of his boat LETHE as though his boat had been turned over in the waters of oblivion. My eyes returned grimly and steadily to his.

"What on earth do you want?" I demanded again. No reply.

By now his hairy paws were back in his boat yet his eyes remained riveted to mine.

"What do you want? Are you deaf?" The gorilla shook its head. Finally a response! For a moment, I thought I was going to scream.

His voice was slow and deliberate, a baritone. "I'm searching this body for..." he said gesturing toward the lake. Whatever apprehension that had begun to show itself in me began equally as fast to disappear.

"For what?" I asked. "What are you looking for?" I repeated. Seconds oozed like molasses in snow.

"The primitive," he replied finally. Enough was truly enough, I thought.

"Oh, the primitive," said I. "That's further down the lake. around that point of rock. You'll see fisherman. His name is James."

"That's where you need to look," I continued. "No primitive here."

No humor rose in those eyes. Only wonderment. His head leaned over as though he were listening for something far away, as of surf breaking on a distant shore. Distance outlined his eyes, an almost misty-eyed rendezvous.

"Truly, the primitive is not here," I repeated. The gorilla nodded as though sad.

He too must have known beneath his hairy coat, in his humorless eyes, the primitive had to be somewhere further away.

"Why can't you simply be a man?" I asked with a sudden, almost unintended curiosity.

"I am not a man. I no longer wish to be. I am a gorilla searching for my home."

His denial struck me as peculiar, especially since he obviously *was* a man inside a gorilla suit.

He thanked me, slipped his oars into the lake, and slowly rowed away. As his boat pulled away, I could make out what seemed to be the boat's full and complete name "Haletheia" printed on the aged stern. Later it was disclosed to my amazement that "Haletheia" was the Greek word for "truth." A vague feeling flowed over me that I would see him again, perhaps on another shore.

His boat soon rowed out of sight; I breathed easier; and now, finally, looked forward to doing some serious fishing on a lazy afternoon. I mused how two people had interrupted this fishing trip. My thoughts turned to James. I wondered if that ape had actually gone to visit him.

Smiling, I thought how it would be for James to have an ape row up to him while he was fishing. Oh, well, I would talk to him later. This lunatic's brew tasted good going down. My toes wiggled in the sunshine; I wanted to get a bass or trout on the line. So far no fish. After baiting again my hook, I cast in.

It was not long before I noticed, to my surprise, another boat round the bend in the cove. I did not believe what I was seeing. Maybe James was playing tricks on me. He had done so before; pranks were his game, especially when his girlfriend Zelda was with him. I rubbed my eyes not once but three times. Each time they saw the same things. There must be some kind of masquerade party going on, I mused. In the distance I could make out what appeared to be a large bird rowing toward me. In fact, it resembled a larger-than-life chicken. My first impulse was to leave. Now. Get out now before another strange bird appeared. But the concoction I had been drinking had slowed me down so that my arms could not obey the impulses from my brain. As its boat neared mine, it became rather apparent that this was no ordinary bird. It was none other than someone dressed as the Crazy Chicken, a bird peculiarly suited to large crowds at professional ball games. This fowl was famed for giving foul hugs and even kisses to total strangers. Yet here there was not a crowd unless you counted the trout, bass, bluegill, and catfish. At ball games, this bird was wont to run madly like some reveling dionysian among the beer drinkers and hot dog lovers and embrace them with its rubbery beak. Visions of such scenes oppressed me as this fowl-burdened boat edged its way toward mine. It had been an eventful day and the prospect of being given a life-smothering bear hug by a man-sized barnyard resident did not excite me in the least. Slowly, ever so slowly, its boat inched closer.

Thoughts of a lazy afternoon of serious fishing began to flee one fish at a time. At this point I could have caught a blue marlin off Cabo San Lucas and it would hardly have phased me. Somehow, in the midst of this moment, I wanted to be almost anywhere but here. With Ernest Hemingway at the running of the bulls in Pamplona; on the veranda with William Faulkner at Rowan Oak; with Kitagawa Utamaro pouring over the purity and beauty of Japanese maidens; with Fyodor Dostoevsky in the middle of Father Alyosha's prayer; with Meister Eckhart preaching to a gathering of nuns at Strasbourg. Anywhere but here.

Just then the chicken stood up and opened its arms as if to hug a long, lost cousin. Bracing myself, I gave it as cold a stare as I could. Some fishing trip, I thought.

"You must be a fan," clucked the chicken, anticipating a country club celebration.

"Oh, no, I'm not. Not me. I don't follow a team," I said. The chicken appeared perplexed like a lawyer who has misplaced her briefs.

"Everyone's a fan of someone," averred the chicken.

"Not everyone," I replied emphatically.

"Even if you're not, you must know me."

"No," I teased. "I don't know who you are at all. Is this a masquerade?"

For a moment the chicken seemed almost downcast.

"I'm the Crazy Chicken. My lawyer just got me a patent on this suit. I rally the team. Hug the bottle-throwing fans!"

"Pleased to meet you," I said, extending my hand. I shook its right wing which was somewhat limp as though lacking in right wing enthusiasm.

"Tell me, are you a he or a she?"

"A she, but many think I'm a he. Some even wish I were only a he," she said, her comb tilted to one side.

"Well, as long as you know who you are, then you've no problems, right?" Expecting the chicken to concur, I breathed easier. However, the chicken demurred.

"You can have problems even if you don't. But fortunately I do know who I am. I am a chicken...and proud of it," she said, as her comb tilted now to the other side.

I thought no one on this lake seems to know who they are. I was delighted to be one of the few on the lake who could say I knew who I was. Or was I?

The chicken luckily did not hear my thoughts. I grew more curious.

"Why do you think you're a chicken," I said after a pause.

"Because I'm loved as a chicken. The crowds... they love me."

"Who knows? Maybe you can be loved as a human being, too," I said with an assurance that came from where I did not know.

"You really think so?" she asked as though she were a doll whose arms had been twisted by great expectations once too often.

"Why don't you take off that silly mask?" I ventured. Her red comb swung now over to the other side of her head.

"But you may not like me the way I'm used to... It's just easier to keep it on. Then no one knows who's hugging them as they wolf down their hot dogs and beer. You know how it is with high culture. It's just the play, you know," she said, her plastic eyes big with excitement, as big as one can become within the limits of plastic.

"Oh, c'mon," I prodded, drinking some more of Old Adam's Ale. My aim was to keep this chicken so distracted

108

she would not try something so foolish as to climb in my boat and give *me* a hug or a kiss as though *I* were a fan.

The chicken shook her head. "It takes the fun out of it," she averred.

"I'd really like to know the 'real' you," I said. "I bet you're a nice chicken, I mean person."

"Really, it's much easier this way," declared the chicken. With that she moved closer. Before I could say "unmask that chicken" she had given me a big hug and kiss. That's how close our boats were.

"I didn't really want a hug. Or a kiss for that matter. I'm not even a fan."

"Oh, I know," she bubbled. "But you looked like you needed them. Anyway, time to go. The crowds are waiting, you know. Fame calls."

My relief at watching her boat pull away was nothing short of gargantuan; it had been a somewhat bizarre afternoon. And I had no fish, not even a bite. What would James think? Only the lupines that blanketed the meadows redeemed the day for me. Her boat soon disappeared around that same point of rock. Maybe I should go and find James before another sideshow floats up here, I thought. At first I had difficulty getting out of the boat for my muscles had not moved much in the last few hours. Up the hill I climbed at a slow pace then turned around and gazed back at the boat. Reaching the crest of the hill, I paused again and felt the slight breeze. So far, there was no sign of James at least where I thought he would be fishing. Through a thick portion of tall grass, there was another clearing; moving cautiously and curiously, I came to another path that wound down on the other side of the hill until it came to a clearing. Finally James! His line was in the lake but next to him was the admiral's hat, dancing plume and all. A couple of steps to my right, behind a low-slung branch clustered with leaves, I spied a kayak. The same kayak, the same admiral's hat.

Puzzled, and with a deepening frown, I paused to gather what thoughts I could. What has been going on here? I did not want to think it really was a set of pranks. From behind some tall grass emerged a woman. I stared intently. So familiar it was his girlfriend, Zelda, who sat down next to him. Where did she come from? Maybe that road, that service road, that curved down the hill, the one that was used for fire trucks, was how she came into the scene. Or maybe by boat. But whose boat?

Beneath my puzzled thoughts, I had this sudden gut feeling that between those two, my fishing trip had been one long prank. After all, it was only a month ago that James came to my birthday party dressed as Giggles the Clown, claiming my parents had hired him, which was not true. Disgusted and embarrassed, I squatted low and moved slowly for a better view; I did not see anything but the kayak and the admiral's hat. But wait. A gust of breeze came up and curled into sight was a rowboat but there was no lettering on the stern which spelled the Greek word for "truth." Perhaps the "truth" had been erased.

At this point I decided to leave, to just leave all the gear and bottles in the boat, and make my way back to the resort where we had rented the boat. Making sure no one saw me, I ventured back, past the boat that swayed slightly in the breeze, and trudged up the hill behind the cove that led down into a shallow valley already criss-crossed by the setting sunlight. In the distance, I could see the cafe and resort with the boats tied to three docks that protruded out into the lake and a few people mingling there and here as a small cabin cruiser leaving its wake made its way past the harbor buoy toward the deeper part of the lake.

Soon I'll be sitting at that café, coffee in hand, a clearing in my head, waiting with satisfaction on my face. To see the looks on their faces when James and Zelda go to an empty boat only to find me gone. Now that would be worth framing, a hook worth waiting for.

Whipped Cream

How Barry remembered those long afternoons when sun shafts lanced the curtains of his Victorian-style apartment as he reclined on his bed, puffing on his pipe that had gone out long ago, trying to penetrate the opaque—deliberately he thought—teutonic prose of the philosopher Immanuel Kant's *Critique of Pure Reason*. He would often get to a place where he was just about ready to experience a moment of insight into the postulates of empirical thought or the transcendental deduction of the a priori categories of the understanding when the same relentless and recurring cry of pleasure and pain would shatter the afternoon quietude. Soon he would not even be able to concentrate on, and much less realize, the meaning of this sentence from Kant's *Critique:* "In the understanding there are then pure a priori modes of knowledge which contain the necessary unity of the pure synthesis of imagination in respect of possible appearances. There are the categories, that is, the pure concepts of understanding."

It happened every day and sometimes at night. The swoons came from the apartment directly above his. He was not used to such commotion. First, there would be this incredible sound of someone, a woman's voice, that sounded like someone in distress, a genuine cry for help coupled with the sound of someone who had achieved what Abraham Maslow called a "peak experience," the highest state of ecstasy, by way of crescendo, her voice could reach. It had the aura of an operatic performance. Then, the sound of rhythmic slaps against a chair although after each a voice would sound in unalloyed ecstasy. Finally, after all this there would be these pleasurable sighs followed by murmurings of relief. When all this

111

was over and the voices had bounced off every wall in the building so that it was impossible *not* to hear these goings-on, there would be this piercing silence disturbed only by occasional whimpers and scrapings of furniture being moved about.

This ritual happened each day, especially in the afternoon. So long as he was alone, he dismissed such as an exercise in tomfoolery. After all, he did not particularly mind what others did so long as it did not interfere with his efforts to understand the Transcendental Analytic section of *The Critique of Pure Reason*. However, it was difficult to wade through Kant's labyrinthine prose amid this piping of pleasure. There were times when he was tempted to go up to that apartment and knock on the door but he did not know what he would or should say. Besides, he had read too much of Kafka and had visions of existential disaster, assuming the door was ever opened. He did not, then, see any way, legal or otherwise, to get them to loosen their grips on such afternoon delights. Nor did he want to call the landlady in on it since she usually overreacted like the time the shower head broke and flooded his bathroom. Even the smallest of things would upset her and increase her blood pressure. So he did nothing and for the most part tried to ignore their daily ritual.

Not long after, he and his girlfriend, Cassie, invited two other couples for dinner at his apartment. It was an informal affair in that they were all friends and graduate students in the philosophy department. There was Tom, the red-haired second year student from Nashville, and his wife, Penny. One of Tom's interests was in the later thought of the German philosopher, Friedrich Schelling; Penny was more interested in how Caroline Schlegel fell in love with Schelling and left her husband to marry him. Another was Amy, a first year student who had bailed out of law school in Manitoba the previous year and her husband, Henri, a student in the English Department whose special interest was in the novels of George Eliot.

Cassie fixed cheese fondue, hot dogs, and salad. Each one fixed their own buns. Penny sat on the couch by the open window next to Tom. Amy and Henri sat

112

on another couch with a small buffet table between them. Cassie brought out the hot dogs.

"Mustard anyone?" she asked. Tom and Penny put mustard on their buns. As they quietly chatted about prosaic philosophical concerns such as the role of doubt in the method of Descartes or how to describe Gaston Bachelard's interest in the psychoanalysis of fire, it was not long before the folks upstairs began their evening foray. At first there was the usual sound of moans and clapping, as distinguished from the sound of one hand clapping, slowly at first, then up to a moderate allegro, and finally an all-out appassionato flurry. Barry knew what was coming next. He knew the routine cadenzas as if he was the conductor.

As they sat quietly eating, as philosophy students sometimes do, there was a lull in the conversation about Hegel's dialectical movement of the Absolute or God, exactly the kind of lull that amplifies sound. Just then, almost like clockwork, the excitement began, only this time more loudly than he had ever heard before. He looked at Cassie who had heard about these episodes, but had not actually heard them herself whose eyes were now growing larger than two jumbo blueberry pancakes.

Penny was the first to become aware of the maelstrom upstairs. Sedate and traditional, she was not as adventurous as husband Tom. He could tell she heard it because her eyes slowly rose to the ceiling in wonder as the ecstasy of clashing cymbals continued. Penny was sure she knew what was going on. She had a look of disgust on her face since she had often thought Sumo Wrestling should be outlawed. For his part, Barry began to feel squeamish. Before he knew it, a woman's voice let out a series of whimpers and squeals of pleasure as though she had just won a dinner for two consisting of Louisiana Fried Prawns, hush puppies, cole slaw, and Tennessee River Catfish. This is embarrassing, he thought. Then Tom heard the commotion upstairs. Looking around at first to see if anyone was looking at him looking, his eyes rose to the ceiling, and, in a puckish moment, had a grin on his mug as broad as Brazil.

113

Soon the inevitable: everybody could hear it. Even Henri paused chewing: a faint smile appeared. Cassie slipped a pickle into her bun. Amy was curious then frowned; she assumed another woman was being used.

Steadily the sounds became louder as the woman whimpered and sighed. It was difficult to continue eating pensively under such circumstances; the rhythm was too distracting. Then the woman's voice began to sound like she was truly in distress like the howl of a coyote. A crescendo yielded to decrescendo. Finally, monastic silence.

At this point, eating returned at its natural pace.

"You have some interesting neighbors," commented Tom stoically.

"Yes, they seem to have taken the position of naïve hedonism," observed Barry, "you know that pleasure is the highest good."

"I don't know how *naïve* it is," grumbled Amy.

The oncoming darkness outside began, ever so slowly, to shroud reflections of the day and their conversation, as the evening wore on, took on a more down-to-earth tone.

The Gold Leaves of Autumn

"Now, class, we measure the progression of the economy by means of a price index. Take the year 1929 for example. In that year 96 billion dollars was the total NNP. Now compare that with the depression year of 1933: only 48 billion dollars. Using 100 for the base year 1929, prices dropped off about one-fourth for the year 1933. But you will notice that 1933's purchasing power was not cut exactly in half. Does anyone know why?" asked Dr. Yuan.

The tall boy Akash who sat in the front row raised his hand.

"Can you tell the class, Akash?"

"Yes, sir. Because prices dipped sharply in 1933, the purchasing power was higher than would be expected for that year in comparison with 1929," said Akash.

"That is correct," said the teacher. The classroom droned on with the buzz of student-teacher discussion. It was a dry autumn day with leaves of red and orange beginning to drop off tree limbs and settle in clustered piles on sidewalks. It had been an eventful summer for it was the first time Winslow DeJurnit had ever fallen; in love, that is. Lina Hurdle was pretty, blue-eyed, dish water blond, and somewhat intellectual. That particular quality counted heavily with Winslow since he was made valedictorian of his high school graduating class. It was rather unique for a girl to be intellectual and pretty at the same time. Ah, the days of springtime and love! It was a time to wander through green fields and watch and listen to bubbling streams and write poetry under some shady tree; with your love, of course. Ah, Lina, Lina honey, thought Winslow. These thoughts occupied Winslow's mind throughout most of the day. He daydreamed about her. Then he went to astronomy class.

"Now name the atmospheric layers beginning with the earth's surface and on up in that fashion."

"Sir, I believe it is the troposphere, the stratosphere, and the ionosphere, in that order," came the reply from Seth Hunter.

"That is correct, Seth, excellent answer," commented the professor, Mr. Pennington. "Excellent."

The cabin only cost four dollars a night. And the lake was so blue. In fact, it was as blue as Lina's eyes. The fish were jumping, sending bubbles now and then to the surface. The sun sent its rays onto the backs of the twosome.

"Where do you live?" asked Winslow.

"Laredo."

"Texas?"

"Where else?" boasted Lina. "Where else is there?"

They laughed together.

"What are you doing out here in Arizona?" asked Winslow thoughtfully as he eyed a saguaro cactus on the hillside.

"Oh, I'm just visiting my aunt in Flagstaff for a couple of months. I really like it here, but sometimes it's so hot. Good thing, it's dry, huh?"

"Yeah, you get used to it after awhile," said Winslow.

"How long have you lived here?"

"About nine years. Before that I lived in Idaho; up in Boise. You ever been through that neck of the woods?"

"No," said Lina.

"Tell me. Do you like literature and that sort of stuff?"

"That's my major at the University of Houston. My sister's at North Texas. But I love Houston."

"No kidding. Literature's my meat for sure. You're going to Houston. What year are you?"

"I'll be a freshman this year," said Lina with a look of curiosity.

"Mmmmmmmmm" was his only reaction. The he spoke up again, "You wanna take a canoe out? The lake's so peaceful now; hardly a ripple on it."

"Sure, but how much do they rent for?" asked Lina.

"Fifty cents an hour. I'll go get one okay?"

Lina nodded in agreement.

Dr. Saby Cubbage wrapped her dark fingers around the lectern while showing a slide of Hammurabi, the king of Babylon as she remarked: "The first ethics displayed in this civilization was based on the Code of Hammurabi. In it Hammurabi set down various laws on property rights, personal injuries, family affairs, etc."

The day was crisp with a crackle of September fires and the raking of dry leaves. It was the time when crowds gather as their favorite football teams took to the field and cheer leaders screamed their "sis boom bahs" and confetti seemed as if to come down like rain when one player crossed over the goal line. The time was like turning over a new leaf to spawn young in the spring that was sure to come. But Winslow's thoughts were of the past summer with Lina.

"I just love the water when it's blue, don't you," asked Lina stroking her hand under the foamy wake as the canoe glided through the lake top.

"Yeah, I guesso. But your eyes are bluer and prettier," added Winslow with a twinkle in his eyes. Lina tried to hold back her smile of flattery but did not succeed.

"You have a line for every girl you meet?

"Oh, no, only pretty ones like you." At this point they both smiled at each other and Winslow continued to dip the canoe blade silently into the water and thrust the canoe into a glide. Sitting in the bow of the canoe, Lina gave the impression of a siren, one that Ulysses never met personally. Her blond hair spread in radiant colors over her ears and an occasional breeze would spread it over the half-buried freckles that dotted her turned-up nose. The lake seemed as if to deepen the blue of her eyes and add a certain grace that only still waters would dare to evoke. Winslow steered the canoe about half a mile further and entered a cove hidden by a bend of rock granite. Once reaching the shore, the twosome sat down on a sandy beach that became more rocky as it progressed toward the shoreline. Winslow had brought his portable radio and took it with him to their resting place on the beach. It provided a soft Mozart background. The sun beamed all over, whitening the sands they sat down on.

"Well, I told you what school I was going to and now it's your turn," said Lina.

"I'll be a freshman at the University of Arizona this year. I hope to play baseball there," remarked Winslow with a tinge of uncertainty in his voice.

"If you don't make the team at Arizona, I'll say they outa their minds. You know that? 'Cause a good lookin' guy like you just couldn't be left out," Lina said, her blue eyes twinkling like stars many light years away. It was Winslow's turn to be flattered. His dimpled cheeks turned upward in a hue of ensuing delight. Lina suddenly thought she liked Winslow, his ideas and thoughts captivated and inspired her. Tall and blond, he was the image of her ideal man. His eyes were grey with a tincture of yellowish-green which when graciously mixed formed a canvas for a Van Gogh or a Toulouse-Lautrec. After this afternoon each party plotted to enhance their image in the other's eye. A long silence followed. Winslow changed the channel on the radio. There came a rendition of the beautiful "Canadian Sunset."

"You ever been to Canada?"

"Yeah."

"When I was a little kid. Why do you ask?"

"Oh, just listening to the sound of it reminded me of it. Where did you go in Canada? Or do you remember?"

"Saskatchewan. Maybe Manitoba, I think. My dad's a hunter and we went hunting for moose. He never got one though. Very disappointing. I barely remember anything else except going fishing."

"Have you ever been to the greatest plot of earth in the world?" said Lina with a subtly joking tone in her voice.

"You Texans gotta brag, huh? Alaska's bigger though. So there."

"You're jealous 'cause Arizona's not bigger," said Lina.

"Hmmmmmph," was the only mumbling response. "You know one thing Texas does have is girls. Especially tall ones that are beautiful and slender. If I could thank Texas I thank the state for producing you."

"I think flattery's getting you somewhere, you know that?"

"Oh, really?" said Winslow in feigned naiveté.

"Uh huh," she said. With that she bent over and planted a kiss on his cheek. It was an unexpected event from this Texas belle, but it had happened. Dizzy, passionate thoughts ran through his head. The flame of love had set Winslow's heart on fire. Their hearts were pumping blood at a stepped-up pace and beads of sweat showed on their faces. It was a lover's truth, a nano second of bliss in a vague, uncertain future. As their lips moved closer and closer together, each could feel the hot breath of desire seething through their pulses. Lina's eyes peered longingly into his.

"Uh, Mr. DeJurnit?" No response. "Winslow DeJurnit?" asked Professor Veale. "Uh, Mr. DeJurnit" he repeated. "I asked you to tell me what was the religious symbol of evil as practiced by the ancient Zoroastrian religion of Persia."

"Uh. Uh." was the only response that came from his lips. In a breakthrough of subconscious verities a line of mumbo jumbo blurted from his lips: "The uh price index of a Hammurabi uh lowered prices on the stratosphere and I uh love you Lina."

Professor Veale looked wide-eyed at Mark in puzzled amazement. From snickers and tittering among a few, the rest of the class burst out laughing.

Creative Nonfiction

Autumn in Thoreau Country

October 9, 1975: I left Philly, where I am a student at Temple, this morning and drove up the New Jersey Turnpike and soon passed the New Haven exit. Pheasant-like fans of color map Octobers in New England. Beauty such as this cannot be said, only *seen*, or second-best, *painted* or *photographed*. The latitude of earth and intensity of the sun seem to collaborate to flesh out the vibrancy of orange, red, purple, and yellow colors. This evening I had a maritime platter consisting of steaming scallops, clams, and shrimp at the Congress Inn, where I decided to spend the night, in the pleasant Rhode Island town of Coventry. I thought of Thoreau's words: "There are innumerable avenues to a perception of the truth." Many avenues. But, Henry, what is *the* truth?

October 10: Today I continued on Highway 95 through Boston and on to that historic colonial town of Concord or, as those with a Boston accent call it, "konk-id." Actually the correct pronunciation of this town, first settled in 1635, sounds like "conquered." Although I could have spent time visiting the homes of Hawthorne, Alcott, and Emerson, I was only interested in Thoreau and Walden Pond. After asking in town, since locals are not broadcasting its whereabouts, especially to tourists, I got directions to Walden Pond. Though it was an overcast day, there were moments the sun came through, and I was delighted to finally see the Pond I had read about in high school. There were a couple of fishermen in a canoe and three or four others fishing off shore. It was not in the pristine state I expected from reading Thoreau's book. But, after all, Thoreau's description of the pond was more than a hundred and fifty years ago. I picked up red maple leaves and put some in my pocket. A time for the solitude of meditation on higher things. I took a forty minute walk along a well-worn trail around the pond. After gazing at the sun dancing on the waters, I ventured up a slight slope of land and went inside a nearby replica of Thoreau's one door and one window cabin that he had built for his 1845-1847 stay on Emerson's land two miles south of town. Here Thoreau had penned *Walden*. Such a simple experiment in living it was.

I went back into Concord and paid a visit to the Thoreau Lyceum where his life and writings have become a gallon-sized tourist industry. After browsing through various editions of his works — *The Maine Woods* and *Cape Cod* among them — I bought a work called *Thoreau: Mystic, Prophet, Ecologist* by William Wolf. Enjoyed the Lyceum but realized it was getting late. I found a place to stay for the night in nearby Bedford. On the lawn of the Unitarian-Universalist Church I wrote postcards to my brother Carl and sister Lani. Once it turned chilly, I headed to my room and began reading my new book. Thought of Thoreau again: "Live each season as it passes...grow green with spring, yellow and ripe with autumn."

I was learning to breathe the seasons through my bones.

October 11: Into New Hampshire. Visited Bristol and Newfound Lake again. Though it was drizzling, it was a delight to return to the first place I ever stayed in New England. The lake was calm, the only disturbance being the tiny rain drops on the surface. Autumn colors everywhere. As though a painter whisked colors during the night with a cosmic brush. Autumn in New England is a must for the aesthetically-sensitive soul. I have never seen anything like it. Become acquainted with beauty such as this and you get some idea of God must be like to the holy man.

On to Canaan, New Hampshire where I dined at the Canaan Inn Bed and Breakfast restaurant. The waitress was as beautiful as the autumn leaves; I tried not to stare as I was almost bored to tears by three gossipy women from San Antonio, Texas as the next table. I ate then left.

On to Vermont: a supreme manifestation of color though nearly submerged in a thunderstorm. As I did not wish to spend the night, I drove back to Philly. You guessed it: the city was engulfed by a thunderstorm. Slowly I plodded my way to my apartment to dryness and safety.